Longman Physics homework for Edexcel IGCSE

Patrick Fullick

PEARSON
Longman

Pearson Education
Edinburgh Gate
Harlow
Essex
CM20 2JE

and Associated Companies throughout the world

www.longman.co.uk

ISBN: 978 1 4058 7496 0

Development and editorial by Sue Kearsey
Designed by Redmoor Design, Tavistock, Devon
Cover photograph @ www.istockphoto.com/Duncan Walker
Printed in Great Britain by Henry Ling Ltd., at the Dorset Press, Dorchester, Dorset

Contents

Contents

How to use this book

This homework book is designed to help you practise all the science you need for your GCSE. The questions are arranged to match the chapters in your Student's Book, as shown in the contents list for this book.

The questions will help you to:
- develop your ideas about each topic
- make key notes or diagrams to use when you revise
- practise solving science problems
- get information from tables, charts and graphs
- see how science affects you and your environment.

The questions are graded on each page, starting with simple exercises and getting harder. Higher tier material is clearly marked with square question numbers. Your teacher will tell you which questions to try.

Most of the information you need will be on the page with the questions, including formulae for calculations. Anything else you need will be at the back of the book. The questions are to help you learn, not to try to catch you out.

Remember Don't be content with just writing down an answer. Think carefully – does your answer make sense? Could you explain it to somebody else? As you do each question, you should: read, think, do, check – and finally understand! If you are still in doubt, ask your friends or your teacher, but work through the answer to make sure you really understand how to get there yourself.

1 Forces at work

❶ Unscramble the letters to find words that can be used when we want to describe the way things are moving.

aeltarecec   epdse   toircedin
adncsit   meit   yevoiltc

❷ The table contains data about some cars. Use the data to answer the questions below.

Manufacturer	Model	Weight (kg)	Max. speed (mph)	0–60 mph (s)	Fuel consumption (miles per litre)	Engine size (cc)	Power output (bhp)
Audi	2.8SE	1450	143	8.1	6.6	2771	193
BMW	318tds	1340	113	13.0	10.3	1665	90
Citroen Xantia	2.0iSX	1238	122	9.6	7.3	1998	135
Ford Mondeo	24V Ghia X	1377	131	8.4	6.6	2544	167
Isuzu Trooper	3.2V6 LWB	1880	106	11.4	4.2	3165	174
Lada Samara	1.1 3dr	900	85	16.7	8.2	1099	53
Mazda MX5	1.8i S	990	116	9.9	7.0	1839	130
Nissan Micra	1.3 GX 3dr	810	104	10.6	10.2	1275	75
Porsche	Targa	1370	168	5.2	5.5	3600	285
Rover 216	Sli 5dr	1040	113	8.9	9.0	1589	109

a Which car
   i is the heaviest
   ii uses most fuel
   iii has the highest top speed
   iv accelerates most slowly from 0 to 60 mph
   v is the most powerful?

b Gemma says 'The bigger the engine, the faster the car.'

Draw up a table with three columns, headed 'model', 'engine size (cc)' and '0–60 mph (s)'. Complete your table using data about the cars, putting them in order of engine size. Is Gemma right?

c Each car is driven on a journey of 200 miles.
   i Calculate how much fuel each car would use on this journey.
   ii If a gallon of fuel costs £3.50, calculate the cost of the fuel for the journey for each car.

d Plot bar charts to show the following data for each car. Put the names of the cars on the x-axis for each chart.
   i power output
   ii 0–60mph
   iii maximum speed

e Compare the shape of your three charts. Is there any link between these three ways of measuring the performance of a car? What advice would you give someone buying a car?

❶ Copy and complete these sentences. Use the words below to fill in the gaps.

constant   distance   fast
stationary   steeper

When an object is moving, its speed describes how .... it is travelling. Its movement can be plotted on a ....–time graph. Where the graph is straight, the object is moving at a .... speed. Where the graph is horizontal, the object is .... The .... the slope of the graph, the greater the speed.

❷ Copy the four distance–time graphs and answer the following questions. Explain your answer in each case.

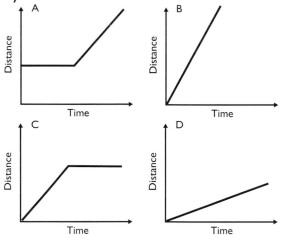

a Which graph shows an object that moves at a steady speed to start with and then slows to a stop?

b Which graph shows an object that is moving at a steady speed faster than all the others?

c Which graph shows an object that is moving at a steady speed slower than all the others?

d Which graph shows an object that is stationary to begin with and then moves away at a steady speed?

❸ Calculate the speed of the following.
a a sprinter who runs 100 m in 10 s
b a ball which moves 18 m in 6 s
c an aeroplane which flies 10 000 m in 50 s
d a car which travels 5.4 km in 30 minutes

❹ The graph shows the movement of a mouse travelling in a straight line.

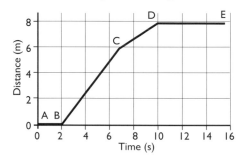

a Describe the movement of the mouse in words.

b Calculate the speed of the mouse between B and C.

c Calculate the speed of the mouse between C and D.

❺ Malik and Susan investigated how fast they could roller skate. The table shows their results.

Time (s)	Distance from start (m)	
	Malik	Susan
0	0	0
2	4	5
4	8	10
6	12	15
8	16	20
10	20	25
12	24	29
14	24	33
16	24	37
18	26	41
20	28	44
22	30	47
24	34	50
26	38	50
28	42	50
30	46	50
32	50	50

Plot a graph of these results using suitable axes. Show clearly which line is Malik's and which is Susan's.

3   Changing direction

❶ Copy and complete these definitions. Use the words below to fill the gaps.

**acceleration   distance   speed
velocity**

a If an object moves in a straight line, how far it is from a certain point is described as the .... it has travelled.

b The .... of an object travelling in a straight line measures how fast it is travelling.

c The .... of an object is its speed in a given direction.

d The .... of an object is the rate at which its velocity changes.

❷ Copy the four velocity–time graphs and then answer the following questions. Explain your answer in each case.

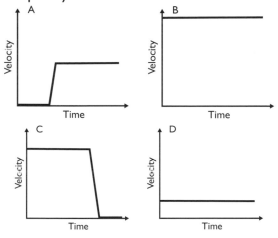

a Which graph shows an object that moves at a steady speed to start with and then slows to a stop?

b Which graph shows an object that is moving at a steady speed faster than all the others?

c Which graph shows an object that is moving at a steady speed slower than all the others?

d Which graph shows an object that is stationary to begin with and then moves away at a steady speed?

❸ The graph shows Hamish's journey to the local shop on foot. Copy the graph. Then copy and complete the table, describing Hamish's motion as clearly as you can.

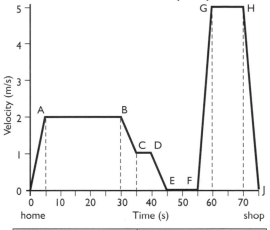

Part of graph	Hamish's motion
0 to A	
A to B	
B to C	
C to D	
D to E	
E to F	
F to G	
G to H	
H to J	

❹ Calculate the following accelerations.

a A cat that increases its speed from 0 to 2 m/s in 1 s.

b A gymnast who increases her speed from 1 m/s to 4 m/s in 0.5 s.

c A car slowing down from 15 m/s to rest in 5 s.

d A cyclist slowing down from 4 m/s to 2.5 m/s in 3 s.

e A bird of prey, hovering and then reaching a diving speed of 12 m/s in 1.5 s.

5 From the graph in **Q3** calculate:

a Hamish's acceleration between each pair of points

b the distance that Hamish travels to the shop.

❶ Copy and complete each sentence using the correct ending from below.

  a To change an object's speed …

  b A push or a pull …

  c When the forces acting on a body cancel out they …

  d When an unbalanced force acts on an object in a particular direction …

  e The motion of an object …

  f The greater the size of an unbalanced force …

Choose endings from

- is called a force.
- the faster an object will speed up or slow down.
- is not affected by balanced forces acting on it.
- an unbalanced force must act on it.
- the speed of the object changes (accelerates) in that direction.
- are said to be balanced.

❷ Copy out these sentences: 'When an object rests on a surface, it pushes downwards on the surface. The surface pushes upwards on the object. The sizes of the two pushes are the same.'

Draw a diagram to show the upwards and downwards forces acting on a book as it rests on the surface of a table. Use arrows like this:

Use the length of each arrow to represent the size of the force.

❸ Look at the diagrams of the cyclists. For each diagram, draw a pair of arrows to show the horizontal forces acting on the bicycle using arrows like this: ➜

Use the length of each arrow to represent the size of the force.

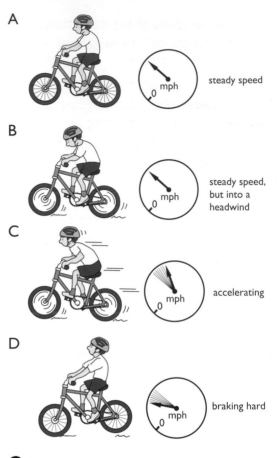

A   steady speed

B   steady speed, but into a headwind

C   accelerating

D   braking hard

❹ The picture shows a race with two go-carts.

  a Draw a diagram to show the horizontal and vertical forces acting on one of the go-carts

    i at the start of the race (when each go-cart has just started to move)

    ii halfway through the race (when each go-cart is travelling at a steady speed).

  b Who do you think will win the race, and why?

5 Applying the brakes

❶ Copy and complete these sentences, choosing the correct phrases from each pair.

Frictional forces always act when **an object is moving/an object is not moving**. These frictional forces are caused by **solid surfaces getting hot/ solid surfaces in contact with one another** and by the resistance of air or water pushing backwards on the object. The direction of the frictional force **is opposite to the direction in which the object is moving/does not depend on the direction in which the object is moving**. The friction between solid surfaces is used **in car engines to produce heat/in car brakes to slow down and stop moving cars**. Friction causes objects to **heat up and wear away/increase their speed**.

❷ Copy and complete the table to show how friction is made as large as possible in some places, and as small as possible in others.

Place	Size of frictional force	How is the frictional force controlled?
car engine		
road surface		
sole of shoe		

❸ When a large passenger airliner lands, you can often see a cloud of smoke coming from the tyres as they first touch the runway. There is very little smoke from the tyres when the runway is wet. Explain these observations.

❹ The Space Shuttle uses a parachute called a 'drag chute' to slow it down after it has landed. Why do you think this method of braking is not used by jet airliners?

❺ The following extract comes from a car advertisement.

'Careful measurements by scientists show that the force of friction between a car tyre and the road surface is at its greatest just before the wheel starts to skid. That's why antilock brakes are so effective, as they apply the brakes hard and release them just before the wheel locks – and they do this many times each second.'

Using text, diagrams or graphs, as necessary, explain as precisely as you can how antilock brakes can stop a car more quickly than brakes not fitted with an antilocking system.

6 Changing shape

❶ Copy and complete each sentence using the correct ending from below.
  a A force …
  b An object will return to its original shape and size when the force is removed if it …
  c Extension …
  d When an object is stretched beyond its elastic limit it …
  e Energy transferred to an object beyond the elastic limit …

Choose endings from
  • is not deformed past its elastic limit.
  • is the amount something has stretched.
  • cannot be got back as useful work.
  • can change the shape of an object.
  • is permanently deformed.

❷ Justin carried out an investigation to see how a spring could be stretched using a force. The graph shows his results.

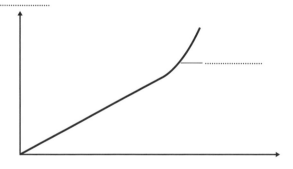

  a Copy the graph and fill in the missing labels.
  b Use the graph to help you to explain why a spring cannot be used any more if you stretch it too far.
  c Using words and diagrams, describe the investigation you think Justin did.

❸ Sangeeta investigated what happened to a piece of elastic when it was stretched. The table at the top right shows her results.

Force (N)	Extension (cm)
0	0
1	1.5
2	3.0
3	4.5
4	6.5
5	9.0

  a Plot a graph of these results.
  b Use your graph to estimate the extension of the elastic for a load of
    i 0.5 N **ii** 4.5 N.

4 Samantha and Panjid carried out an investigation to find out how two different springs stretched. The table shows their results.

Force (N)	Length (cm)	
	Spring 1	Spring 2
0	5.0	7.2
2	7.6	10.4
4	10.2	13.6
6	12.8	16.8
8	15.4	20.3
10	18.5	24.2

  a Use these results to produce a graph to show the behaviour of the springs.
  b Barry hung a weight on one of the springs. If the length of the spring was 13.2 cm, what possible values could the weight have had?
  c Barry took the weights off both springs and then connected them together one underneath the other. He then hung a 5 N weight on them. How much did they stretch altogether?

7 Driving around

1 a Copy and complete these sentences. (You will need to add more than one word to complete each case.)
  i Thinking distance is the distance the vehicle travels …
  ii Braking distance is the distance the vehicle travels …
  iii If you add the thinking distance to the braking distance you get the …
b Write down two factors that increase
  i thinking distance
  ii braking distance.

2 'Only a fool breaks the two second rule' is a saying designed to help car drivers leave a large enough gap between their car and the car in front. A two-second gap is the distance travelled by a car in two seconds. The table shows some stopping distances for cars travelling at different speeds.

Speed (m/s)	Total stopping distance (m)	Two-second gap (m)
11	12	
27	53	
37	96	

a Complete the table to show what a two second gap is for each speed.
b Does a two-second gap provide a safe stopping distance for each speed in the table? Explain your answer.
c When might you have to leave a larger gap, even at slower speeds?

3 A car accelerates from rest up to a steady speed. A short time later, the brakes are applied, the car slows down, and then travels at a steady speed again. The energy transferred by the car was originally stored in its fuel
a Draw a diagram to show the energy transfers when
  i the car accelerates
  ii the cars slows down.
b When the car eventually stops, what will have happened to the energy from the mixture of fuel and air burnt in the engine?

4 Answer the following questions, using the relationship
force (N) = mass (kg) × acceleration (m/s²).
a A car has a mass of 750 kg and accelerates at a rate of 3 m/s². What is the size of the unbalanced force acting on it?
b Two people are pushing a car. The mass of the car is 500 kg, and the unbalanced force acting on it is 750 N. What is its acceleration?
c A car accelerates at a rate of 0.5 m/s². Its engine exerts an unbalanced force of 300 N. What is the car's mass?

❶ Copy and complete these sentences. Use the words below to fill in the gaps.

area   increases   limit   pressure   stretch

Modern cars have many safety features. Padding inside the car helps to reduce the .... exerted by these parts of the car on the driver's body in an accident, by spreading the force over a bigger .... An airbag may help to protect the driver even more. As the driver's body compresses the gas in the bag, its pressure ....The bag pushes back on the driver's body, helping to slow it down. Seatbelts also help to slow the driver down. They .... as they stop the driver moving. This takes them beyond their elastic ...., so they must be replaced when the car is repaired after a serious accident.

❷ Using words and diagrams, explain why crash barriers and cycle helmets are designed so that they are permanently deformed when they are damaged in an accident.

❸ a Copy the diagram and fill in the missing labels to show the safety features fitted to this car.

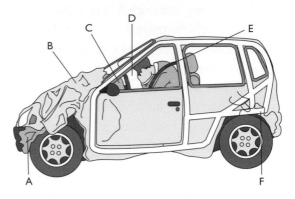

b Suggest other safety features that could be added. Explain your choices, using diagrams or graphs and words.

❹ Use the graph below to explain why wearing a seatbelt protects a passenger in a car when they are involved in a collision. Be as precise as you can, and use the data from the graph to make your points clearly.

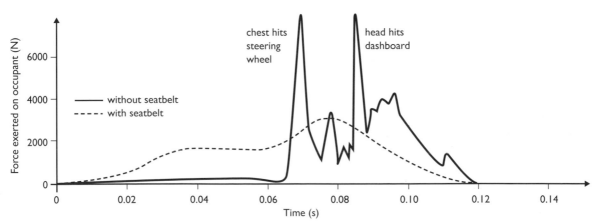

9 Falling freely

❶ Calculate the weight of the following at the surface of the Earth, using the relationship

weight (N) = mass (kg) × gravitational field strength (N/kg)

Take the gravitational field strength at the surface of the Earth as 10 N/kg.

a 2 kg Christmas pudding
b 750 kg car
c 45 kg person

❷ Copy and complete the table to show the details of the mass and weight of a spacecraft. (The Earth's gravitational field is about six times that of the Moon.)

	At Earth's surface	At Moon's surface	In deep space
mass	6000 kg		
weight			

3 Copy and complete these sentences. Use the words below to fill in the gaps.

**accelerates   frictional   terminal
gravitational   mass   newtons**

Wherever it is, an object always has the same ...., which is measured in kilograms. In a .... field it will also have weight, which is measured in .... There is a gravitational field around the Earth, which .... falling objects. As the speed of a falling object increases, ... forces increase until they balance the gravitational force. When this happens, the balanced forces acting on the object mean that its speed does not increase any more – it has reached .... velocity.

4 Look at the pictures of the skydiver and force arrows. List the letters to show the correct order of pictures.

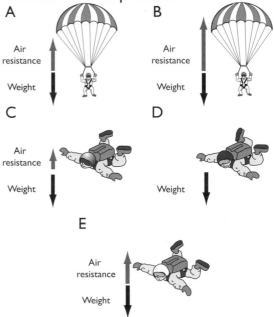

A
Air resistance
Weight

B
Air resistance
Weight

C
Air resistance
Weight

D
Weight

E
Air resistance
Weight

5 Describe how a parachute makes it possible to jump out of an aeroplane safely. Use the following words.

**terminal velocity   air resistance
frictional forces   weight**

1 The diagram shows a balanced see-saw.

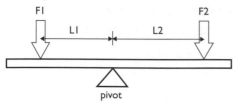

a Write down the moment of the force F1 about the fulcrum. State clearly whether this moment is clockwise or anticlockwise.

b Write down the moment of the force F2 about the fulcrum. State clearly whether this moment is clockwise or anticlockwise.

c Write down the relationship between these two moments when the see-saw is balanced.

d If F1 = 50 N, L1 = 0.25 m and L2 = 0.20 m, calculate the size of F2.

2 The diagram shows a wheelbarrow. The wheelbarrow and its load weigh 600 N; this force acts vertically at a distance of 40 cm from the axle of the wheelbarrow.

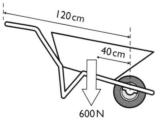

What force must be applied to the handle of the wheelbarrow to lift the wheelbarrow and load?

3 A screwdriver is used to lever the lid off a tin of paint. A force of 25 N is exerted at right-angles to the end of the screwdriver, 20 cm from the point at which the screwdriver rests on the can (the pivot). What moment does this force exert about the pivot?

4 A nut on a car engine must be tightened using a turning force of 220 Nm. A spanner 40 cm long is available. What force must be applied perpendicular to the end of the spanner to produce this turning force?

5 The diagram shows a ruler being balanced on a finger in two different ways.

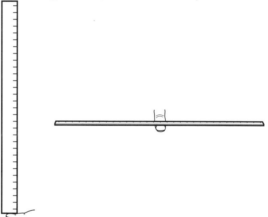

Which way is easier to balance the ruler and why?

6 A gardener wishes to weigh some fertiliser using a shovel balanced across a log. The shovel has a mass of 5.0 kg, and balances at a point 60 cm from the handle and 40 cm from the other end.

The gardener puts some fertiliser onto the shovel. It now balances at a point 70 cm from the handle and 30 cm from the other end. If the weight of the fertiliser acts 10 cm from the end of the shovel, what mass of fertiliser was put onto the shovel?

11 Mains electricity

❶ Copy and complete these sentences. Use the words below to fill the gaps.

direct   alternating   batteries   backwards

The current always flows in the same direction in the electricity from .... This is called .... current (d.c.). In mains electricity the current direction switches .... and forwards 50 times a second. This is called .... current.

❷ Copy the diagram of a mains cable. Use the labels below in place of A–D on your diagram.

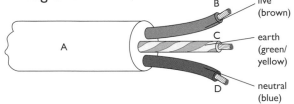

- flexible plastic case for insulation
- copper wires to conduct electricity
- colour coded for identification
- twisted thin wires for flexibility

❸ Daisy has two electric drills in her workshop. They have the following information stamped on them.

drill A	drill B
240 V	12 V
a.c.	d.c.
50 Hz	

a Which of these drill works directly from the mains?

b Explain the three terms on drill A.

c What might drill B run on?

d Which drill needs thicker insulation? Explain your answer.

e Which drill might need an earth wire in its cable? Explain your answer.

f Which drill would be safe to use in the rain? Explain your answer.

❹ Look at this diagram of a correctly wired mains plug. Match the labels below with the letters A–E on the diagram.

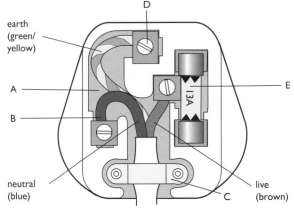

- wires correctly positioned
- insulation cut back just enough – no bare wire showing
- cable clamp secure
- screws tightened
- correct fuse fitted

❺ This plug has been incorrectly (and dangerously) connected. List as many faults as you can (there are seven to find).

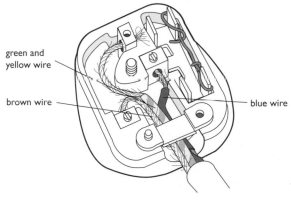

WRONG AND VERY DANGEROUS

❶ Copy and complete these sentences. Use the words below to fill the gaps.

contract   electricity   heart   wet

High voltage .... can be very dangerous. If you get an electric shock, the electricity makes your muscles .... If this affects your ...., it could kill you. If your hands or feet are ...., more current flows through you so the danger is very much greater.

❷ Copy and complete these sentences, choosing the correct word from each pair.

In mains electricity, the **live/neutral** wire provides the voltage that drives the current. If you touch a **live/neutral** wire you will get a shock. So switches should always be connected to the **live/neutral** wire. If the live and neutral wires are reversed in a plug, the equipment **will/ will not** work, but it will not be safe.

❸ Look at the diagrams. Match the labels below with A–F, to explain why the live and neutral wires must not be reversed.

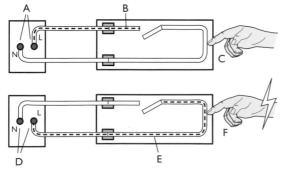

- the rest of the wire is live, even when the switch is open
- live current stops at the open switch
- if you touch the wire, you will get a shock
- incorrectly wired
- the rest of the wire is safe if touched
- correctly wired

❹ Fuses are connected in the live wire. If too great a current passes, they 'blow', switching off the circuit. Look at the diagrams. Match the labels below with A–E on the diagram, to explain how fuses work.

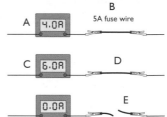

- overload
- fuse wire breaks, breaking the circuit
- fuse wire cold
- working current
- fuse wire heats up

❺ Fuses come in set values: 13 A, 5 A and 2 A. Copy and complete this table by adding the appropriate fuse to use in the plug.

Equipment	Working current	Fuse
two-bar fire	8A	**a**
radio	0.1A	**b**
vacuum cleaner	3A	**c**
freezer	2.5A	**d**
small cooker	12A	**e**
150 W bulb	0.6A	**f**

❻ Rearrange these sentences to explain how a circuit breaker can protect you from a shock. Copy the sentences out in the correct order.

- The circuit breaker detects that the current in the live wire is no longer the same as the current in the neutral wire.
- If a fault occurs, some current leaks through the earth wire – or through you.
- The circuit breaker very quickly switches off the current.
- Normally the current in the live wire is the same as the current in the neutral wire.

13 Calculating electrical power

❶ This equation shows how to calculate the power in an electrical circuit.

power (W) = voltage (V) × current (A)
(watts)   (volts)   (amps)

Use the equation to calculate the power of a motor that runs on 10 V and takes a 2 A current.

❷ a Copy the table showing current, voltage and power data from various electrical circuits. Use the formula from **Q1** to calculate the missing values.

Voltage (V)	Current (A)	Power (W)
230	10	**i**
230	0.25	**ii**
12	5	**iii**
110	**iv**	1100
24	**v**	12
1.5	**vi**	6
vii	5	30
viii	3	72
ix	0.1	23

b Which three entries could refer to 'mains' circuits? Explain your answer.
c Which fuse would you use in each circuit from part **b**? (Choose from 2 A, 5 A or 13 A.)
d Which entry might be an electric kettle circuit? Explain your answer.
e Which might be an electric light bulb circuit? Explain your answer.

❸ A car battery supplies electric current at a voltage of 12 V. What energy is transferred from the battery when a current of 0.5 A flows for 180 s?

❹ A torch uses two 1.5 V cells connected together in series. It is switched on for 10 minutes. During this time 360 J of energy are transferred from the batteries to the bulb in the torch.
a Calculate the voltage produced by the two cells in series.
b What current flows through the cells during the time the torch is switched on?

1 Copy and complete the sentence, choosing the correct word from each pair. You should be able to do this in two different ways, to make two correct sentences.

Like/unlike charges **repel/attract**.

2 A freshly rubbed comb will pick up small pieces of paper. Copy the diagram. Use the labels below in place of A–D on your diagram.

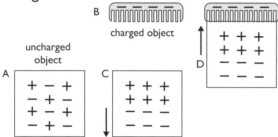

- The remaining positive charges are attracted to the comb.
- A charged comb has an excess of negative charges.
- The comb charge repels the negative charges on the paper.
- A unchanged object has positive and negative charges.

3 Copy and complete these sentences, choosing the correct words from each pair.

If you touch a charged van der Graaf generator, your hair **stands on end/lies flat**. This is because all the hairs become charged with **the same/different** charges, and these **unlike/like** charges repel each other.

4 Use the idea of static electricity to explain the following situations.

a Electrostatics are used to ensure that spray paint spreads out evenly. (Clue: the paint droplets all pick up the same charge.)

b Your hair can sometimes stand up in a thunderstorm or when you take off a nylon jumper.

5 Look at the diagram of a Van de Graaff generator. Match the labels below with A–C on the diagram to explain what is happening.

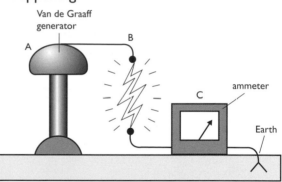

- Once the voltage is high enough, a spark will jump the air gap.
- Electric current is detected as electrons flow through the metal wire to earth.
- As charge builds up on the dome, the voltage increases.

1 Copy and complete these sentences. Use the words below to fill the gaps.
attract   electrically   static

When materials such as wool and nylon are rubbed together, they become .... charged. They can .... and pick up small pieces of paper near them. This type of electricity is called .... electricity.

2 From the list below, copy out those effects that are caused by static electricity.
- Nylon jumpers make a crackling sound when you pull them off.
- TV screens get dusty very quickly.
- Fridge magnets stick to fridge doors.
- Balloons stick to the wall if you rub them on your jumper.
- Lightning is common during heavy storms.
- Suction caps stick to mirrors.
- You can get an electric shock from a metal object if you have just walked over a nylon carpet.
- You can get an electric shock from a bare wire on the 'mains'.

3 Rearrange these sentences to explain what causes static electricity. Copy them out in the correct order.
- The material that loses some negative charges becomes positively charged overall.
- These charges usually balance out.
- If enough charges build up, they can jump back together, causing a spark.
- The material that gains extra negative charges becomes negatively charged overall.
- If you rub two materials together, negative charges may be knocked from one to the other.
- Opposite charges attract one another.
- All substances carry both positive (+) and negative (−) charges.

4 Abdul performed an experiment to see which materials produced the largest electrostatic effect. He did this by rubbing each material with a dry duster and then gradually lowering it into some crispy rice cereal, until they were attracted up to it. The larger the electrostatic effect, the higher the crispy rice 'jumped'. Here are his results.

Material	Height jumped (cm)
nylon comb	10
glass rod	5
cellulose acetate	8
ebonite rod	7
perspex ruler	3

a Which material showed the greatest static effect?

b Plot a bar chart of Abdul's results.

5 Look at the diagram of a simple photocopying process. Match the labels below with A–D on the diagram.

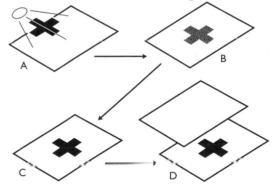

- Dry ink powder is attracted to the charge.
- The ink is transferred to paper.
- This leaves a negative image in the charge.
- Light falls on to a special charged material.

6 Hospitals use flammable chemicals such as ether that could be ignited by static sparks. A trolley with rubber wheels could get charged up enough by the movement of blankets or sheets to cause such a spark. Hospital trolleys now have a short length of chain dangling from the metal frame to the floor to stop this.

16 What else is involved?

① Copy and complete these sentences. Use the words below to fill the gaps.

conductors current electrons insulators

Static charges can build up on .... as they do not allow the charges to move easily. Metals are not like this. They allow small negatively charged particles called .... to move through them. They are .... A flow of moving electrons is called an electrical ....

② Electrons need an energy output from some kind of 'electron pump' to make them flow around a circuit. Link the following 'electron pumps' to the energy source that drives them. Copy out your answers.

'electron pump'	energy source
generator	sound
battery	light
microphone	movement (kinetic)
solar cell	chemical

③ Look at diagrams A and B. Bulbs have a coil made of resistance wire in them.

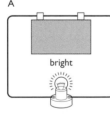
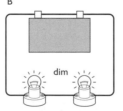

a Explain why the bulb in circuit A gets hot when electricity passes through it.

b The bulbs in circuit B are the same as in circuit A. Is more or less current flowing through circuit B than circuit A? How can you tell?

c If a third bulb was added into circuit B, would the brightness of the bulbs increase or decrease? Explain your answer.

d If a second battery was added to circuit A, would the bulb get brighter or dimmer? Explain your answer.

e What would happen if the wire in circuit A was broken?

④ Dimmer switches have a coil of resistance wire in them, and a sliding contact that can make the electricity pass through all or just part of the wire.

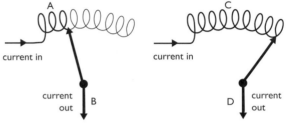

Copy the diagrams. Use the labels below in place of A–D on your diagram.

* This gives a low current and dim light.
* This gives a high current and bright light.
* Long wire gives high resistance.
* Short wire gives low resistance.

⑤ A single cell provides a potential difference of about 1.5 V. Cells can be stacked up to increase the voltage, but if they are connected the wrong way around, they can cancel each other out.

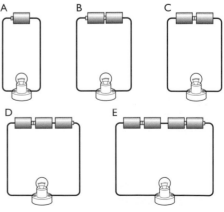

a What voltage will be provided in each of the circuits A–E?

b How many of these cells would there be in a 12 V dry battery?

1 Copy and complete these sentences. Use the words below to fill the gaps.

parallel   series

A circuit where all the components are in a single loop is called a .... circuit. If the circuit has two or more loops, it is called a .... circuit.

2 Copy these circuits and say whether they are series or parallel.

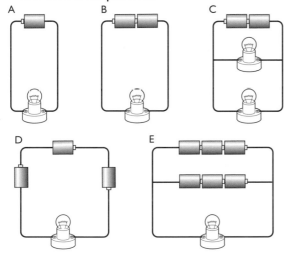

3 Copy the following symbols. Use the words below to explain what each symbol stands for.

A

B

C

D

E

F

(A)

G

(V)

resistor   voltmeter
variable resistor   ammeter
switch (open)   lamp   cell

4 Describe the following simple circuits in words.

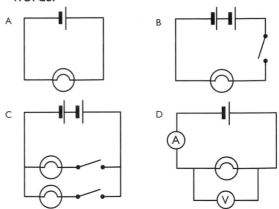

5 Draw simple circuit diagrams for each of the following.

  a two bulbs in a simple series circuit with two cells

  b a bulb with one cell and a variable resistor

  c an ammeter in series with a resistor and a cell; a voltmeter in parallel across the resistor

  d two bulbs in parallel with a single cell; an open switch in the main loop of the circuit

6 Which bulbs, if any, would light up in each of circuits A–D?

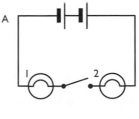

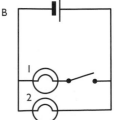

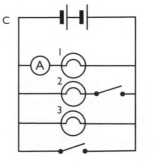

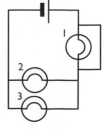

18 Measuring electricity

1 Copy and complete these sentences, choosing the correct word from each pair.

The size of the **current/voltage** flowing in a simple circuit depends on the resistance. A low resistance lets a **low/high** current flow. The size of the current also depends on the voltage. The higher the voltage the **higher/lower** the current.

2 In a circuit, what would happen to the size of the current if you
  a doubled the voltage
  b doubled the resistance
  c multiplied the resistance by 10?

3 Look at the graph that shows how the current in a circuit varies with voltage.

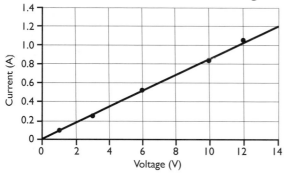

  a Describe in words how the current varies with the voltage.
  b What is the current at 6 V?
  c What would the current be at 8 V?
  d What current would you expect at 14 V?
  e What voltage gives a current at 1 A?
  f What is the resistance of this circuit? (Use your answer to part **d**, and the formula resistance = voltage/current.)

4 Look at the diagram.

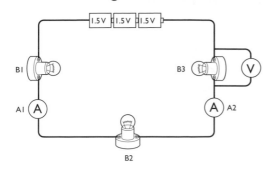

  a What is the total voltage from the three cells?
  b If ammeter A1 reads 0.5 A, what is the current at A2?
  c The three bulbs are identical and B1 has a resistance of 3 ohms. What is the total resistance of the three bulbs in the circuit?
  d If voltmeter V reads 1.5 V, what would the reading be across bulb B1?
  e A current of 0.5 A flows through B3. Calculate its resistance (resistance = voltage/current). Does this agree with part **c**?

5 In this diagram, B1, B2 and B3 are identical 4 ohm bulbs.

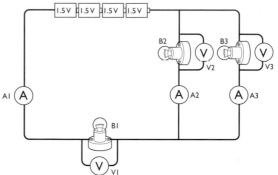

  a Is this a series or parallel circuit?
  b If ammeter A1 reads 1 A, what is the current through A2?
  c What is the current through A3?
  d What is the total voltage provided by the four cells?
  e Voltmeter V2 reads 2 V. What does V3 read?
  f What must V1 read?
  g Is the *combined* resistance of bulbs B2 and B3 larger, smaller or equal to that of bulb B1?

1 Copy and complete these sentences, choosing the correct word from each pair.

A **resistor/diode** allows current to flow in either direction. A **resistor/diode** allows current to flow in one direction only.

2 This circuit was used to test both a lamp and diode. Each component was placed in position X. Each component was connected one way and then the connections were reversed. The voltage was changed at the power supply. The current and voltage readings are shown in the table.

power supply 0–12 V

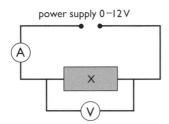

Voltage (V)	Current in component A (amps)		Current in component B (amps)	
	normal	reversed	normal	reversed
0	0	0	0	0
2	0.4	−0.4	0.2	0
4	0.7	−0.7	0.4	0
6	0.87	−0.87	0.6	0
8	0.95	−0.95	0.8	0
10	1.0	−1.0	1.0	0

a Plot the results for component A on a graph with axes like these.

+A

−V ———————— +V

−A

b Plot the results for component B on a similar graph.

c Label your graphs 'lamp' or 'diode' as appropriate.

d For your 'lamp' graph, describe the way the current varies as the voltage increases. Explain why this is happening.

e For your 'diode' graph, how do you know that this graph represents a diode?

f Describe how the current varies with voltage when the diode is connected the right way around.

g Resistance in ohms = voltage (V) / current (A).
What is the resistance of the lamp at 2 V?

h Calculate the resistance for the lamp at 4 V, 6 V, 8 V and 10 V.

i Plot a graph of resistance against voltage for the lamp.

j What is the resistance of the diode when it is connected the right way around?

3 Copy and complete the table showing the power rating and current used by some different electrical appliances when connected to a mains supply of 220 V.

Appliance	Power rating (W)	Operating current (A)
vacuum cleaner	1100	**a**
dishwasher	2640	**b**
electric shower	**c**	25
hairdryer	880	4
food mixer	**d**	1
lamp	55	**e**

1 Jamil measured the current through and the voltage across a resistor. The table shows his results.

Voltage (V)	Current (A)
2.50	0.04
4.10	0.07
5.90	0.10
9.70	0.16
11.50	0.19

a Plot a graph of his results, with voltage as the x-axis.

b Draw a straight line of best fit through the points.

c Comment on the accuracy of Jamil's readings.

d Use the graph to estimate the current at 8 V.

e Extrapolate the graph to estimate the likely current at 15 V.

f Do you think your answer to part **e** is as reliable as your answer to part **d**? Explain your answer.

g Construct lines on your graph and use them to work out the resistance of the resistor.

h Sketch in and label the line you would expect for a resistor of double the resistance.

i Sketch in and label the line you would expect for a resistor of half the resistance.

2 Look at the graph that shows how the resistance of a certain thermistor drops with temperature.

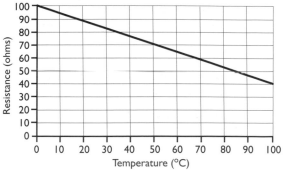

a What is the resistance at 75 °C?

b At which temperature is the resistance 85 ohms?

c What current would flow through the thermistor circuit at 0 °C if it were connected to a 12 V battery?

The thermistor could be set up as part of a frost prevention circuit for a greenhouse, as shown below. The computer would sense the current flowing in the circuit.

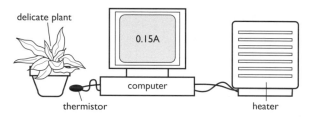

d How would the computer know when to switch the heater on?

e If the temperature must not rise above 25 °C, how would the computer know when to switch the heater off?

f Draw a conversion graph for current against temperature for this circuit when connected to a 12V battery.

3 The voltage of a car battery is measured as it supplies different amounts of current, with the results shown in the table below.

Current (A)	0	10	20	30	40	50
Voltage (V)	12	11.4	10.8	10.2	9.6	9.0

a Plot a graph of these results.

b Use your graph to estimate the voltage of the battery if it supplies a current of 100 A.

c What assumption(s) did you make in answering part **b**?

d If a car's headlights are switched on before the engine is started, the lights dim when the starter motor is operated. Use these results to explain this.

21 Waves – what are they?

❶ Copy and complete these sentences. Use words from below to fill the gaps.
amplitude   energy   frequency wavelength

a A wave transfers .... from one place to another.

b The .... of a wave is the distance from a peak or trough to the undisturbed position.

c The .... of a wave describes the distance between a particular point on one disturbance and the same point on the next.

d The number of waves passing a particular point in one second is called the ....

❷ Look at the diagram of a water wave.

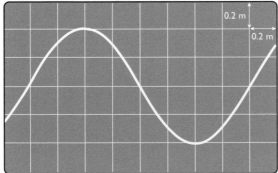

0.2 m

0.2 m

a What is the wave's amplitude?

b What is the wave's wavelength?

❸ a Draw a water wave with an amplitude of 2 cm and a wavelength of 5 cm.

b Draw a water wave with an amplitude and a frequency each double the value of the wave in part **a**.

❹ A boy pushes a ball up and down on the surface of a swimming pool to produce a wave, as shown in the picture.

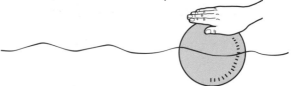

a The boy moves the ball further up and down, at the same rate as before. What happens to

 i the amplitude of the waves produced

 ii the wavelength of the waves produced

 iii the frequency of the waves produced?

b The boy moves the ball up and down the same amount as originally, but faster. What happens to

 i the amplitude of the waves produced

 ii the wavelength of the waves produced

 iii the frequency of the waves produced?

5 'The wave which travels along a rope is a transverse wave.'

a What is a transverse wave?

b How must you move the end of a long piece of rope in order to produce a transverse wave?

c Which way do the particles in the rope move?

6 Explain why ripples on a pond make a leaf bob up and down, but the leaf hardly moves from side to side.

1 When waves on the surface of the sea travel towards the shore, they tend to meet the shore almost at right angles. Use the idea of refraction to explain this.

2 The waves used in a microwave oven have a wavelength of 12.2 cm and a frequency of 2450 million hertz. Calculate the speed of the waves. Use the formula

wave speed (m/s) = frequency (Hz) × wavelength (λ)

3 Waves on the surface of the sea are travelling at a speed of 20 m/s with a wavelength of 200 m. What is their frequency?

4 Sound waves travel through seawater at about 1500 m/s. If the frequency of a sound wave travelling through the sea is 300 Hz, what is its wavelength?

5 Copy and complete the table, suggesting what sort of wave might be involved in each case.

Wave speed (m/s)	Frequency of wave (Hz)	Wavelength of wave (m)	Type of wave
3	a	10	b
c	2 000 000	1 500	d
340	170	e	f

6 a Copy and complete the diagrams showing the behaviour of water waves passing through a gap.

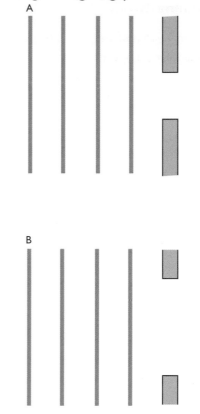

A

B

b What is the name given to this kind of behaviour?

23 The radiation family

❶ Copy and complete these sentences. Use the words below to fill in the gaps.

**energy   electromagnetic   speed
straight   waves**

The Sun radiates energy, which is sometimes called .... radiation. Different types of radiation are given different names, and carry different amounts of .... All of them move as ...., and travel in .... lines at the same ....

❷ Pair up the statements about electromagnetic radiations so that the second statement follows from the first.

Statement 1

a All electromagnetic radiations travel as waves.

b All electromagnetic radiations travel at the same speed.

c All electromagnetic radiations travel in straight lines.

d All electromagnetic radiations can travel through space.

Statement 2

• The electromagnetic radiations behave in similar ways.

• Infra-red radiation from the Sun can reach the Earth.

• Radio waves travel at the speed of light.

• It is impossible to see round corners.

❸ Electromagnetic waves travel through space at 300 000 km/s. Calculate how long it would take an electromagnetic wave to do these journeys.

a From a transmitter on the Earth to a satellite 30 000 km above the Earth's surface.

b From the Moon to the Earth (about 390 000 km).

c From the Sun to the Earth (about 150 million km).

❹ The family of electromagnetic waves includes radio waves, microwaves, infra-red radiation, light and ultraviolet radiation.

Look at the picture below and replace the letters with labels to show where each type of radiation is being used.

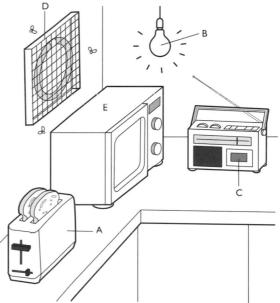

❺ A light-year is a measure of distance. It is the distance travelled by light in one year. If light travels at 300 000 km/s, how far is a light year in km?

6 Winston sits watching an athletics event on television. The TV signal travels via satellite a total distance of 73 500 km. Winston hears the official fire the starting gun at exactly the same time as Joan, who is sitting 85 m from the gun at the athletics ground. Take the velocity of sound as 340 m/s, and the velocity of electromagnetic waves as 300 000 km/s.

a How far from the television set is Winston sitting?

b What assumptions have you made in answering this question?

24 Using radiation

① Match each type of electromagnetic radiation with one of its uses, then copy them out.

Radiation	Uses
X-rays	cook food under a grill
radio waves	are visible to the eye
infra-red waves	can be used to see inside a person's body
light waves	have wavelengths longer than about 10 cm
gamma rays	help produce a sun tan
ultraviolet waves	cook food by transferring energy to water molecules
microwaves	are given off by some radioactive substances

② Microwave ovens are designed with special safety features so that microwave radiation cannot get out of the oven when it is switched on. Explain why this is necessary for the safety of the person using the oven. [Hint: think how the oven cooks food.]

③ The picture shows a rescue worker using thermal imaging equipment to help find people in a collapsed building. Explain how equipment like this enables rescuers to detect people.

④ When someone stands under a 'light' giving off ultraviolet radiation at a party or a disco their clothes may glow. Explain why.

⑤ The 'protection factor' of a sunscreen is a guide to how much protection it can give you against ultraviolet radiation. For example, 'Factor 6' sunscreen should allow you to stay out in the sun roughly six times longer than if you were not wearing any sunscreen at all.

Sunscreen factor	no sun screen worn	2	6	15	24
Maximum safe time in sunshine (min)	15	i	ii	iii	iv

  a Copy and complete the table.
  b In practice, it may not be safe to stay out in the sunshine for as long as these times indicate. Why not?

⑥ A person stands in front of a photographic film. A beam of X-rays is directed at them. Explain the following.
  a The film shows the person's skeleton in white against a black background.
  b The person must take off any metal objects such as brooches or pendants before having the X-ray.
  c The person's exposure to X-rays is kept to a minimum.

1 Copy and complete the sentences and diagram. Use the words below to fill in the gaps (one word is used more than once).
change direction   speed   refracted ray   normal   incident ray

When light travels from one transparent material to another it may .... This happens when the .... of light in one material is different to the .... of light in the other.

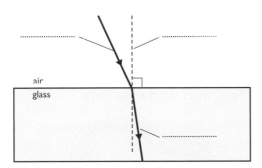

2 Light bends towards the normal when it travels from air into glass, and away from the normal when it travels from glass into air. Copy and complete the diagram of a ray of green light entering a triangular prism to show what happens when the light travels through the prism.

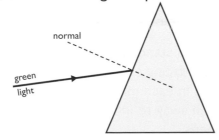

3 The diagram shows a ray of white light entering a prism.

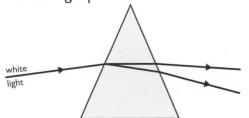

a Light of seven different colours emerges from the prism. Explain why.
b Two rays are shown coming out of the prism. One is red, the other is violet. Which is which?

4 A ray of light is shone through a semi-circular glass block. Use the diagram to explain the following.

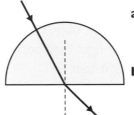

a The ray is not refracted as it enters the glass.
b The ray is refracted away from the normal as it leaves the block.

At a certain angle the refracted ray travels along the bottom of the glass.

c What is this angle called?
d What happens when the angle of incidence is greater than the angle in part **c**?
e If the refractive index of the block is 1.5, calculate the value of the angle in part **c**.

5 Draw diagrams to show how light travels along an optical fibre
a when the fibre is straight
b when it curves through an angle of 90°.

6 A periscope can be made from two prisms like the one shown in the diagram.

Draw a diagram showing how the prisms must be arranged so that someone can see over the heads of a crowd. Show the path of the light through the prisms using rays with arrows on them.

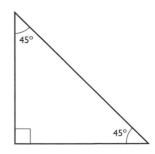

1 Copy and complete these sentences. Use the words below to fill in the gaps.

**absorbed   darker   light
reflected   Sun**

Waves can be .... from hard surfaces. We see many objects because .... is reflected from them and enters our eyes. We see other objects, like the ...., because they give out their own light. When an object reflects light, some of the light may be .... The less light that is reflected, the .... the object appears.

2 The diagram shows three light waves striking a surface. One light wave has been reflected. Copy and complete the diagram to show the path of light waves A and B after reflection.

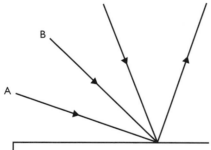

3 A simple party trick involves sitting someone at a table, on which is a cup with a coin in it. The coin is just out of sight of the person, below the rim of the cup. (The person is asked to say what the coin is, without moving themselves or the cup.) How can they do it? (Hint: a jug of water is placed on the table for them to use.)

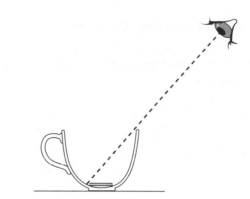

Draw a diagram to explain your suggestion. If in doubt, try the trick yourself!

4 The diagram shows a ray of light passing along an optical fibre. Explain why the ray of light stays inside the fibre.

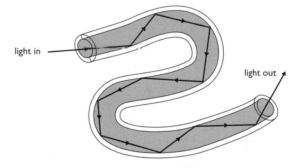

5 Draw a diagram to show what happens when a ray of light strikes a plane mirror at an angle of 45°.

6 A person standing between two plane mirrors facing each other sees a series of images in each mirror which appear to stretch away to infinity. Explain how this happens.

7 A ray of light enters a water at an angle of 30° to the normal. It is refracted so that it makes an angle of 22.2° with the normal in the water.
   a Calculate the refractive index of water.
   b Calculate the critical angle at the water/air boundary.

1 Copy and complete these sentences. Use the words below to fill in the gaps.

energy microphone oscilloscope vibrating

Like all waves, sound waves transfer .... This energy comes from objects that are .... Sound waves can be detected by your ear, and by a .... If this is connected to an ...., a 'picture' of the sound wave can be obtained.

2 The diagrams show three oscilloscope traces produced by three different sound waves. The sounds are
  a low pitch and loud
  b low pitch and quiet
  c high pitch and quiet.

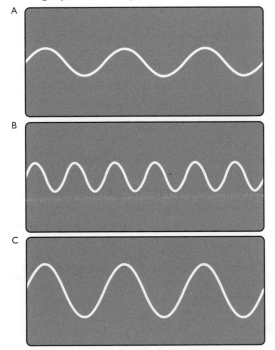

Copy the three traces and write the correct description under each one.

3 The 'string telephone' is a popular child's toy. It can be made from two plastic cups, joined together by a length of string.

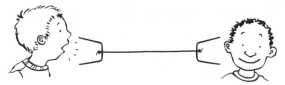

  a Explain how the telephone works.
  b Why must the string be tight?
  c Why does the telephone stop working if someone holds the string?
  d How could two of these string telephones be used so that one person could talk to three other people?

4 A pupil standing opposite a tall building 500 m away blows a short, loud blast on a whistle. The time from the blast to the echo is 3.0 s. What is the speed of sound?

5 A person sitting in a metal boat hits the hull of the boat, producing a sound wave that travels though the water and through the air.

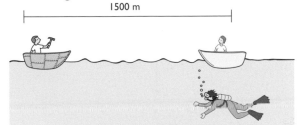

1500 m

  a How long will the sound take to reach someone sitting in a second boat 1500 m away?
  b How much sooner will the sound be heard by a diver in the water underneath the second boat?
  (Speed of sound in air = 340 m/s, speed of sound in water = 1500 m/s)

6 Some teachers claim to be able to see round corners! Explain why it is possible to hear round corners when it is not possible to see round them.

❶ Copy and complete these sentences. Use the words below to fill in the gaps.

20 000 Hz   bats   echolocation
echo   hear   ultrasound

When sound is reflected it is called an .... Some animals, like .... make use of sound to 'see' – this is called .... They produce pulses of very high-pitched sound, called ...., which has a frequency of more than .... Humans cannot .... these pulses.

❷ Use the diagram of a fishing trawler using pulses of sound to locate shoals of fish to help answer the questions. Take the speed of sound in water as 1500 m/s.

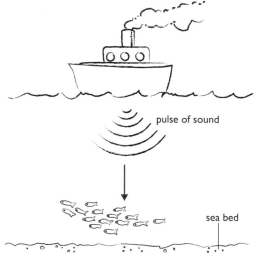

pulse of sound

sea bed

a A pulse of sound is produced by the trawler. It travels down through the sea and bounces off the sea bed, returning to the trawler 0.2 s after it was produced. What is the depth of the sea? (Remember that the pulse goes down to the sea bed and back in 0.2 s.)

b How long after the pulse was produced would an echo be heard if it bounces off a shoal of fish 50 m below the surface?

c A trawler produces a pulse of ultrasound, and two echoes are heard: one after 0.1 s, another after 0.4 s. Suggest an explanation for this.

❸ The diagram shows the Whispering Gallery in St Paul's Cathedral in London, which is circular. A person sitting on one side of the gallery can whisper a message along the wall of the gallery, which will be heard by another person sitting with their ear next to the wall on the opposite side of the gallery. Copy the diagram and use the idea of reflection to complete it.

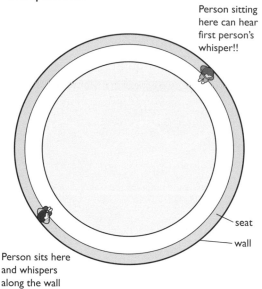

Person sitting here can hear first person's whisper!!

seat

wall

Person sits here and whispers along the wall

❹ A person shouts at a cliff and hears an echo exactly 3 seconds later. If the person is standing 500 m from the cliff, what is the speed of sound through air?

❺ A tsunami is a wave produced by a disturbance that displaces a large amount of water, travels very fast, and has a wavelength that is very large. If a tsunami has a wavelength of 500 km and a frequency of 0.0005 Hz, what is its speed?

29 What is energy?

1 Copy and complete these sentences. Use the words below to fill the gaps.

**electrical   energy   light
kinetic   sound**

There are many forms of ....
The Sun emits .... and heat
energy. Loudspeakers gives out
.... energy. A moving car has
.... energy. Batteries or 'the
mains' provide .... energy.

2 Make a list of all the different forms of energy you can see in this picture.

3 Some forms of energy are active – you can see something happening. Other forms of energy are stored and need to be 'released' in some way.

Copy and complete the table, using the types of energy from the list below.

Active energy	Stored energy

- chemical energy
- potential energy
- electrical energy
- light energy
- kinetic energy
- heat energy

4 Stored energy can be turned into active energy. Copy and complete the following sentences. Choose the correct form of energy from each pair.

a Natural gas contains stored **chemical/elastic** energy. This turns into **heat/electrical** energy when it burns.

b A clockwork motor contains stored **chemical/mechanical** energy. It turns into **light/kinetic** energy when the spring unwinds.

c A cell contains stored **chemical/mechanical** energy. It turns into **electrical/kinetic** energy when the wires are connected.

d Petrol contains stored **chemical/mechanical** energy. It turns into **light/kinetic** energy when it explodes in the engines and makes the car move.

e A stretched bow contains stored **chemical/ mechanical** energy. It turns into **heat/kinetic** energy when the bow is released.

5 Copy and complete these sentences choosing the correct word from each pair. For each part of the question you should be able to make two correct sentences.

a A **microphone/loudspeaker** turns **electrical/sound** energy into **electrical/sound** energy.

b An electric **motor/generator** turns **electrical/kinetic** energy into **electrical/kinetic** energy.

c A solar **cell/light bulb** turns **electrical/ light** energy into **electrical/light** energy.

d A roller-coaster free-rolling **up/down** turns **potential/kinetic** energy into **potential/kinetic** energy.

1 Electric fires are very efficient, as 99% of the electrical energy is turned into useful heat energy. Petrol engines are far less efficient, as only about 35% of the stored chemical energy is turned into useful kinetic energy. Of the rest 5% is released as sound and the rest is 'waste' as heat energy.

a Draw Sankey diagrams to show the percentage energy conversions in electric fires and petrol engines.

b For each of the following electrical devices, suggest what has happened to the 'missing' energy.

  i light bulb: electricity → 8% light +

      ....

  ii food mixer: electricity → 50% kinetic energy + ...

  iii transformer: mains electricity → 90% 12V electricity + ...

  iv vacuum cleaner: electricity → 70% kinetic energy + ...

c **i** Arrange the energy changes from part **b** in order of increasing efficiency.

  ii Display this information as an efficiency bar chart.

2 Copy this formula

efficiency = useful energy output (J)
                       —————————————
                        total energy input (J)

Use this formula to calculate the efficiency of the following devices. Show your working.

a It takes 500 J of energy to push a box up a ramp (total energy input). However, the box only gains 300 J of potential energy (useful energy output).

b It only takes 400 J to roll a barrel up the same ramp, giving the same gain in potential energy (300 J).

c It takes a total energy input of 750 J to lift a 600 N bucket of water by 1 m (a useful energy output of 600 J) using a pulley.

3 Screw-thread car jacks were used to lift a 10 000 N car by 10 cm.

a What was the change in potential energy?

b The total amount of energy used to crank up the jacks was 20 000 J. What was the efficiency?

c These car jacks are not very efficient as they have to overcome a lot of friction in the screw-thread. What form of energy do you think the 'wasted' part has turned into?

d Hydraulic car jacks are more efficient. A hydraulic jack lifted the same car to the same height. Its 32 W electric motor had to run for 40 seconds to do this. Use the equation
energy (J) = power (W) × time (s)
to work out how much energy the motor needed to do this.

e Calculate the efficiency of the hydraulic jack.

4 a A conventional, coal-fired power station 'loses' 9% of its energy when the fuel is first burnt. For every 1 MJ of stored chemical energy in the coal

  i how much is 'lost' at this stage

  ii how much remains?

b Gas-fired power stations are more efficient at this stage, losing only 5%. How much energy is 'kept' in this case from every 1 MJ?

c Of this retained energy from part **b**, 53% is lost as waste heat in the cooling towers. How much energy (in kJ) remains after this stage?

d If another 46 kJ is lost in the generator plant, how much electrical energy is produced?

e Heat exchangers can trap some 'waste' energy and use it to heat water greenhouses or homes. If the heat exchangers are 90% efficient, how much additional could be 'saved' from the original 1 MJ in a gas-fired power station, using your figures from part **c**?

1 Copy and complete these sentences. Use the word below to fill the gaps.

**conductors   convection   currents
poor   radiation**

Metals are good .... of heat energy. The heat energy is passed along the solid. Liquids and gases are .... conductors but, if heated from below, moving .... are set up which move the heat energy by ....

Hot things also give out heat energy as 'heat rays' or ....This is the only way that heat energy can pass through empty space. It is how we get energy from the Sun.

2 Poor conductors are called insulators. Copy and complete the table using the materials from the list below.

Conductors	Insulators

**copper   wood   aluminium   ice
silver   plastic   glass   brass**

3 Explain the following situations.

a Frying pans are made of metal, but the handles are made of plastic or wood.

b Stainless steel cups are not very good for drinking hot drinks from.

c Hot serving dishes may be put on to a cork mat rather than straight onto a polished table.

4 Look at the diagram of the kettle. Match the labels below it with A–D, to explain how water is heated by convection.

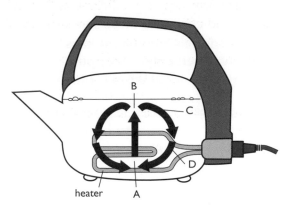

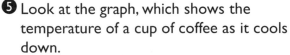

- The water cools and contracts.
- The water is heated and expands.
- It sinks back down, passing back over the heater.
- The hot water floats up through the cooler water.

5 Look at the graph, which shows the temperature of a cup of coffee as it cools down.

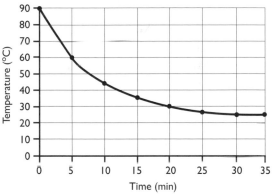

a What is the temperature after 5 minutes?

b How much did the temperature drop in the first 5 minutes?

c How much did the temperature drop in the second 5 minutes?

d Why was there a bigger temperature drop in the first 5 minutes than in the second 5 minutes?

e What do you think the temperature would be after 40 minutes? Explain your answer.

1 Copy and complete these sentences. Use the words below to fill the gaps.

**bubbles   energy   trapped
radiation   insulators   fibres**

Wasted heat .... wastes money. We use .... to help stop heat energy escaping. Air is a good insulator if it is .... so that it cannot move. Air can be trapped in .... in expanded polystyrene, or between the .... of a woolly jumper. Shiny silver surfaces help to reduce heat loss by ....

2 Look at the diagram of a vacuum flask. Match the labels below with A–D on the diagram.

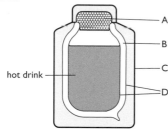

- Vacuum to stop heat loss by conduction and convection.
- Hollow, double-layered glass bottle, with silvered surfaces to reduce heat loss by radiation.
- Hard case to protect the glass.
- Plastic or cork lid to stop heat loss by conduction through the top.

3 Terry and Seehra set up an experiment like this.

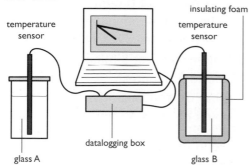

They put hot water into the two glasses and started the datalogging program. Here is the graph that the computer produced.

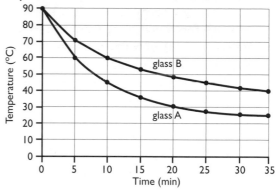

a What was the water temperature in glass A after 10 minutes?

b What was the water temperature in glass B after 10 minutes?

c Why is the water temperature in glass B higher than that in glass A?

d What is the difference in temperature after 35 minutes?

e What do you think the difference in temperature would be after 1 hour? Explain your answer.

4 Julie and Anton performed an experiment similar to that in **Q3** using two metal cans without insulation.

a Use their results to plot a graph.

Time (min)	Can A (°C)	Can B (°C)
0	90	90
5	60	70
10	43	58
15	33	50
20	27	44
25	25	39
30	25	35

b One of their cans had a shiny silver surface, while the other had been painted matt black. Which can was which? Explain your answer.

33 Heat transfer

1 **a** Rearrange these sentences to explain how heat energy is conducted along a metal rod. Copy the sentences out in the correct order.

- In this way, energy is transferred through the metal, away from the source.
- When a metal is heated, these electrons move faster.
- In metals, some of the electrons can move from atom to atom, forming a 'sea' of electrons.
- These faster electrons spread out through the metal.
- Atoms have tiny charged particles called electrons whizzing around the nucleus.
- The electrons collide with other particles, and some of their energy is transferred.

b Draw a simple diagram to show this effect in action.

2 **a** The heat energy from the Sun reaches us by radiation. How do you know that it does not reach us by conduction or convection?

b Which part of the electromagnetic spectrum transfers heat energy?

c In hot and sunny countries, such as Greece, houses are often painted white. What advantage does this have?

d The water pipe in solar panels are painted matt black. Explain why.

e Chinese take-away meals are often served in shiny aluminium containers. Aluminium is a very good conductor, so why do these meals stay hot for a long while?

3 Use your understanding of conduction, convection and radiation to explain the following.

a Peter's bedroom is in the attic of his house. The room has a very large, south-facing window set into the roof which cannot be opened. The room gets very hot and stuffy in the summer.

b Jacqui had a fall on a mountainside and couldn't move. She was trapped out in the open on a cold night. She survived by lying on a pile of dry grass and wrapping herself in a silver 'space blanket'.

c Rescuers searched all night for Jacqui using a thermal imaging camera, which picks up body head radiation. The rescuers failed to find Jacqui. Why was that?

4 The diagram shows a greenhouse, with the Sun shining on it. Radiation with wavelengths close to the wavelengths of visible light can pass through glass. Radiation with wavelengths longer or shorter than this is reflected.

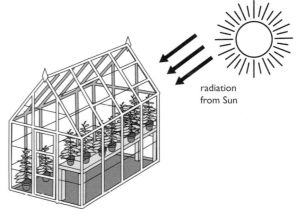

radiation from Sun

a Some radiation from the Sun can pass into the greenhouse. What effect will this have on the temperature of things inside the greenhouse and why?

b Things inside the greenhouse emit infra-red radiation with a wavelength longer than that of visible light. What will happen when this radiation reaches the glass in the greenhouse?

c Use your answers to parts **a** and **b** to explain how a greenhouse works.

d In the Earth's atmosphere, carbon dioxide and other gases behave like the glass in a greenhouse. How can this information be used to explain the rise in the Earth's temperature over the last 50 years?

1 Copy and complete these sentences. Use the words below to fill the gaps.

continuous   expensive   fossil heating

Nearly 90% of the energy used in the average home goes on .... and hot water. This energy may be obtained by burning .... fuels – coal, oil or gas. Gas that is most commonly used as a .... supply may be piped in. Electricity is also used. This is very convenient but can be more ....

2 This pie chart shows how heat is lost from a typical home.

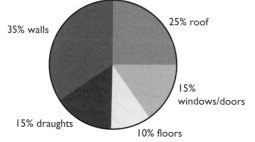

35% walls
25% roof
15% windows/doors
10% floors
15% draughts

a Which part of the house loses the most heat?

b More heat is lost through 1 m² of window than 1 m² of wall. Explain why window heat loss is less important overall.

c A house costs £500 a year to heat. How much is 'wasted' due to draughts? (Assume all this lost energy may be saved.)

d A firm gives an estimate of £150 to fit draught excluders. How long would it take for the savings on heat loss to 'pay' for this expenditure?

e The owner decides to fit the draught excluders herself. She has worked out that she will get her money back in 8 months. How much must the draught excluders cost to buy?

f The owner knows that double glazing would reduce energy loss through the windows by a half, but she is quoted £2250 to do the job. Is this a good idea in terms of potential savings? Explain your answer.

3 Cavity walls can be filled with different kinds of insulating material to reduce heat loss. The fillers are 'rated' for different purposes in the chart below, where 5 = good, 4 = quite good, 3 = reasonable, 2 = not very good, 1 = poor)

The categories in the table are:

- **Env**: environmental impact – good means no problem
- **Health**: associated health problems – good means no problem
- **Energy**: how good it is for saving energy
- **Use**: how easy/reliable it is to use

Material	Env	Health	Energy	Use
fibreglass	4	2	4	5
mineral wool	5	3	4	5
cellulose	5	4	5	4
polystyrene	3	4	4	4
polyurethane	3	3	5	4
vermiculite	4	3	3	4

a Copy the table. Add an extra column for 'total score' and fill in this column.

b Which material gets the best total score?

c Draw a bar chart for the total score value of these materials.

d Cellulose filler is made from recycled paper. Do you think its environment score would be so high if it were not recycled? Explain your answer.

e Polystyrene and polyurethane are made from oil. Which low values does this explain? Explain your answer.

f Polystyrene can be recycled. How would this affect its 'total score' ?

g Some old houses were built with hollow cavity walls. Today, insulation is fitted as the walls are built. Most insulation comes as blocks or sheets, but polyurethane foam is squirted in as a liquid, which then bubbles, swells and sets. Explain why polyurethane foam is sometimes used to insulate the empty cavities in these older houses, despite its 'lower' total score.

35 Movement and energy

1 Copy and complete these sentences. Use the words below to fill in the gaps.
energy force fuel hot joules work

When an object is moved by a force, the force does .... and energy is transferred. The engine in a car provides the .... to make the car move. The moving car has kinetic energy. This energy comes from the mixture of .... and air which is burnt in the engine. When the driver brakes, the car slows down and the brakes get .... as .... is transferred from the car to the brakes. Both energy and work are measured in ....

2 **a** Use this relationship to calculate the following.
work done (J) = force (N) × distance moved in direction of force (m)
  i the work done when a person lifts a 1 kg bag of sugar a distance of 2 m
  ii the work done when a 50 kg person climbs a flight of stairs 5 m high
b Where does the energy to do this work come from in each case?

3 Copy out these sentences, choosing the correct bold words from each choice.
a As an object travels faster, its kinetic energy **stays the same/gets smaller/gets larger**.
b Two objects with different masses are travelling at the same speed. The kinetic energy of the larger mass is **the same as/greater than/less than** the kinetic energy of the smaller mass.
c A clockwork mouse is wound up and released. As it speeds up, the energy stored in the spring inside the mouse **decreases/does not change/increases**.

4 Kinetic energy is calculated using the formula
kinetic energy (J) = ½ × mass (kg) × (velocity (m/s))^2

A bullet has a mass of 0.025 kg and leaves the barrel of a gun at 300 m/s. A jet airliner has a mass of 150 000 kg and also travels at 300 m/s.
a Calculate their kinetic energies.
b Explain why their kinetic energies are different, even though they are travelling at the same speed.

5 A 'superball' with a mass of 0.1 kg is lifted from the ground to a height of 2 m.
a Calculate the energy transferred to the ball in lifting it to this height.
b The ball is released. What will be its kinetic energy just before it hits the ground?
c The ball hits the ground and rebounds to a height of 1.8 m. Calculate the energy stored in the ball at this height.
d What was the kinetic energy of the ball just after it rebounded?
e Explain the difference between your answers to parts **b** and **d**.

6 The change in gravitational potential energy is given by the formula:
change in gravitational potential energy (J) = weight (N) × change in vertical height (m)

Calculate the change in gravitational potential energy in each of the following cases.
a Jack weighs 400 N. He falls 10 m vertically off a ladder.
b A 25 N cat is hoisted 20 m out of a well.
c A volcano blasts a 100 N block of lava 300 m into the air.
d A 1 N spanner falls 200 m from a skyscraper.

1 Look at the diagram of a power station. Which of the labels below could be used to replace the letters A–E? Copy the labels out in the correct order, to explain how the power station works.

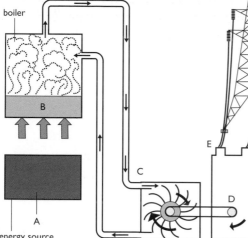

boiler

B

A

energy source

- The generator produces electricity.
- Expanding steam turns the turbine.
- The fuel is burnt to give heat energy.
- The turbine spins the generator.
- This boils the water.

2 Look at the diagram of a solar panel. Which of the labels at the top right could be used to replace the letters A–E? Copy the labels out in the correct order to explain how the solar panel works.

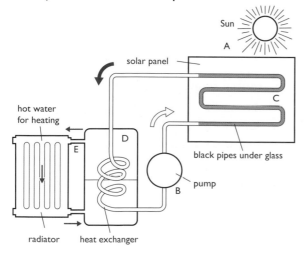

Sun

A

solar panel

C

hot water for heating

E

D

black pipes under glass

B

pump

radiator   heat exchanger

- The heated water passes through a heat exchanger.
- The water in the pipes is heated.
- Cold water is pumped into the panel
- Hot water is produced for heating.
- Sunlight shines on the solar panel.

3 Copy and complete these sentences. Use the words below to fill the gaps.

hydroelectric   kinetic   potential turbines

Water high in the mountains has lots of gravitational .... energy. This turns to .... energy as the water flows downhill. The energy in flowing water can be used to turn .... and generate electricity. This happens in .... power stations.

4 The diagram shows a barrage across the Rance estuary in France. It generates 250 MW of electricity. Which of the labels below could be used to replace the letters A–D? Copy the labels out in the correct order to explain how the Rance barrage works.

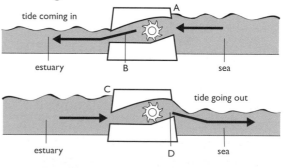

tide coming in

A

estuary   B   sea

C   tide going out

estuary   D   sea

- This flows out through the turbines, spinning them again to produce electricity.
- The turbines spin generators and produce electricity.
- As the tide goes out, water is trapped behind the barrage.
- As the tide comes in, water is forced through the turbines.

1 A nuclear reactor has the following features. Match each feature with its purpose, and then copy out the complete sentence.

a A fuel rod …

b A thick concrete case …

c A reactor core …

d Liquid sodium in pipes …

Choose from the following purposes.

- picks up the heat energy from reactor and carries it out.
- contains uranium or plutonium fuel.
- stops the harmful radiation escaping.
- is where the reaction takes place with the fuel in the rods.

2 The amount of electrical power used in any part of the country varies with the time of day.

a Plot a graph of the power usage in one region using the data in the table.

Time (24-hr clock)	Power used (GW) (1 GW = 1000 MW)
00.00/24.00	5
06.00	5
09.00	8
10.00	7
18.00	7
19.00	9
22.00	8

b Suggest why demand varies like this.

3 Hydroelectric power plants can be switched on or off in minutes, but conventional fossil fuel stations have to be kept running all the time. If they are shut down, they take days to start up again.

The region described in **Q2** has six 1 GW fossil fuel power stations, two 1 GW hydroelectric power stations and is connected to the National Grid. Use this information and the 'power used' table from **Q2** to answer the following questions.

a The six fossil fuel stations are kept on all night. Why not shut one down to save energy?

b How is the demand for power at 09.00 hr met?

c What do you think happens at 10.00 hr?

d At what time does the region have to buy in extra electricity from the National Grid?

4 Energy from sunlight can be as much as 1 kW per square metre.

a How much energy would fall onto a square kilometre at this rate? (1 km² = 1000 m × 1000 m)

b In practice, the average value will be much less, perhaps just 10% of the maximum value. List some possible reasons for this.

c Calculate the average power falling on 1 km².

d Solar cells are only 25% efficient. What power output would you get from 1 km² of these?

5 A barrage could be built across the Severn estuary, between England and Wales. It would be nearly 20 km long with over 200 turbines, each capable of producing 40 MW.

a How far apart would the turbines be on average?

b What would the power output be?

c A typical power station has a 1 GW output. How many power stations would this barrage be equivalent to?

d The projected cost for this scheme is £8000 million. A new gas-fired power station would cost about £500 million. Is the barrage worth building on simple economic grounds? Explain your answer.

e Why, in the long term, is it worth considering?

38 Spreading forces

1 Explain the following.

   a Vehicles that are designed to travel over soft ground have wide tyres.

   b A wide plank of wood can be used to rescue a person who has fallen through thin ice.

   c A drawing pin has a small point at one end and a broad top at the other end.

2 A person leans against a wall, pressing on it with the palm of one hand, which has an area of 50 cm².

   a If they exert a force of 200 N on the wall, calculate the pressure they exert on the wall, using the formula pressure = force / area. Write your answer using the correct units.

   b Instead of pressing on the wall with the palm of one hand, the person now reduces the force they exert on the wall to 50 N, pressing on it with one fingertip which has an area of 1 cm². Calculate the new pressure exerted on the wall.

3 The deepest part of the ocean is thought to be the Marianas Trench in the Pacific Ocean, which is 11 000 m deep.

   a If seawater has a density of 1030 kg/m³, what is the water pressure at this depth?

   b What force would this pressure exert on each 1 cm² area of a fish living at this depth?

4 The base of a metal container measures 50 cm × 80 cm. Some concrete is poured into the container to a depth of 50 cm. The concrete has a mass of 480 kg.

   a What is the volume of the concrete?

   b Calculate the density of the concrete.

   c Calculate the area of the base of the container.

   d What pressure does the concrete exert on the base of the container?

5 A giraffe's head is a vertical distance of 2.5 m above its heart. If the density of the giraffe's blood is 1000 kg/m³, what pressure must the giraffe's heart produce in order to pump blood to its brain?

6 Here are two possible designs for a hydraulic system designed to lift a weight of 720 N.

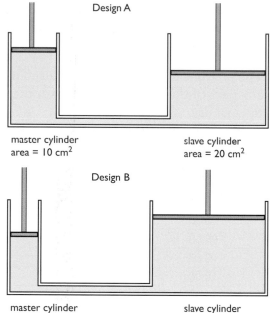

Design A

master cylinder area = 10 cm²   slave cylinder area = 20 cm²

Design B

master cylinder area = 5 cm²   slave cylinder area = 40 cm²

   a What is the advantage of design A over design B?

   b What is the advantage of design B over design A?

7 Airliners have pressurised cabins so passengers are more comfortable at altitudes of 10 000 m or more, where the air pressure outside the aircraft is 28 kPa. If the pressure in the cabin is 100 kPa, what is the resultant force on a cabin door with an area of 2 m² in the side of an airliner?

39 Matter

1 Copy the three diagrams. Write the correct caption under each diagram, choosing the correct word from those shown in bold.

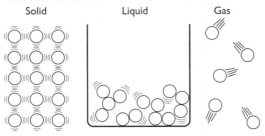

Solid   Liquid   Gas

a In a **liquid/solid/gas**, the particles are close together but are free to move about.

b In a **liquid/solid/gas**, the particles are close together and are held in place but they can still vibrate.

c In a **liquid/solid/gas**, the particles are far apart and are moving at high speed.

2 Explain the following.

a A gas fills any container into which it is put, and exerts a force on the walls of the container.

b The pressure of a gas rises if it is heated and not allowed to expand.

c Smoke particles observed under a microscope move around in a jerky way, sometimes described as a 'drunk's walk'.

3 Explain why a hot air balloon rises. You will need to include
* what happens to the gas particles when they are heated
* what this does to the volume of gas
* what this does to the density of the gas
* what effect altering the density of the gas has.

4 Copy this diagram of a radiator in a room. Label your diagram, using a similar series of ideas to those in **Q3** for the first part of your explanation.

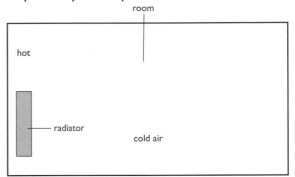

5 A balloon is filled with air to a pressure of 1 atm. It has a volume of 1200 cm³. The balloon is taken up a mountain to a height where the atmospheric pressure is 0.6 atm. What is the volume of the balloon here?

6 The pressure of the gas in an oxygen cylinder is 300 atm. The cylinder has a volume of 0.4 m³. What volume would the oxygen occupy if it was let out of the cylinder into the atmosphere?

7 The stated pressure for the air in a car tyre is 250 kPa at 20 °C. If the temperature of the air in the tyre increases to 32 °C, what will be the pressure of the air in the tyre?

8 The pressure exerted by the Earth's atmosphere is equivalent to a column of water 10 m high. An air bubble 90 m below the surface of a lake has a volume of 2.5 cm³. What will be its volume just below the surface of the water?

① Copy and complete these sentences. Use the words to fill the gaps.

magnet   north   pole   repelled
south   steel

A .... will line up north–south if it is free to move. The end that points .... is called the north-seeking .... Magnets attract iron and ....The north pole of one magnet will attract the .... pole of another, but if one magnet is turned round it will be ....

② Copy and complete this sentence. Choose the correct word from each pair. You should be able to do this in two different ways, to make two correct sentences.

Like/unlike poles **repel/attract**.

③ Copy the diagrams below. Say whether there would be attraction or repulsion in each case.

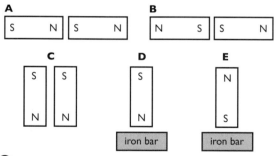

④ The magnetic field around a magnet can be seen by sprinkling iron filings over it. A small compass needle will follow these lines.

Copy the diagram below. Show the direction in which a compass needle would point in the positions shown (one has been done for you).

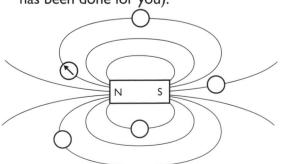

⑤ Hardeep made an electromagnet from a coil of wire, using 10 turns, and connected it up as shown below.

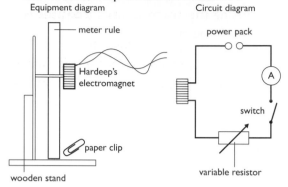

She investigated the strength of the electromagnet for different currents by seeing how high the electromagnet had to be moved before it would no longer make the paper clip jump up to it.

Current	Maximum height jumped (mm)
0.3	11
0.6	20
1.0	35
1.5	50
1.6	42
2.0	72

a Plot a scatter graph of her results, showing current against maximum height jumped.

b Her friend Suzie changed the resistor in the middle of one reading, so Hardeep wrote down the wrong current value. Draw a circle around this anomaly (the point that does not fit the pattern).

c Draw a best fit straight line through the rest of the points.

d Describe the relationship between the maximum height jumped and the current.

e Sketch in a new line to suggest the results you might expect if she repeated the experiment using 20 turns instead of 10.

f Eric did a similar experiment, but wound his coils around an iron nail which he left in place. Would his electromagnet have been stronger or weaker? Explain your answer.

1 Copy and complete these sentences. Use the words below to fill the gaps.

electromagnets   iron   permanent

Unlike .... magnets, ... can be switched off. This is very useful for buzzers and relays, as well as the giant magnets used to lift scrap ....

2 Look at the car starter motor circuit.

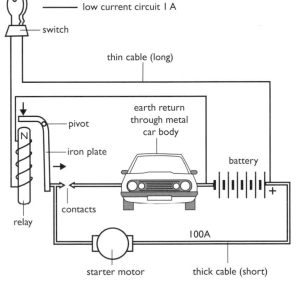

a What happens to the relay coil when the switch is turned on?

b What happens to the top of the pivoted iron plate?

c What happens to the contacts after part **b**?

d What happens to the starter motor after part **c**?

e Why does the starter motor circuit need thicker cable than the switch circuit?

3 An electron travels through a magnetic field without changing direction. Draw a diagram to show the direction of movement of the electron and the direction of the magnetic field.

4 a Rearrange the sentences to describe how the buzzer works. Copy the sentences out in the correct order.

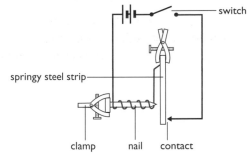

- This breaks the circuit at the contact.
- The springy steel vibrates backwards and forwards as the current is switched on and off at the contact.
- When the switch is closed, current flows in the circuit.
- The steel springs back, making the circuit again.
- The springy steel is attracted to the electromagnet.
- The coil becomes an electromagnet.
- The coil loses its magnetism.

b Why is the coil of the electromagnet wound round an iron nail?

5 Rearrange the sentences to explain how a loudspeaker works. Copy the sentences out in the correct order.

- The coil becomes an electromagnet, its strength varying with the current.
- The coil moves a paper cone in and out.
- This makes the coil move backwards and forwards, to the same pattern as the electrical signal.
- The moving paper cone makes the air vibrate, creating sound waves.
- A varying force occurs between the electromagnet and the permanent magnet.
- A variable electrical signal is passed through a coil that is held in a magnetic field from a permanent magnet.

❶ Copy and complete the sentences using the correct word from each pair. You should be able to make two correct sentences.

A **generator/motor** turns **kinetic/electrical** energy into **kinetic/electrical** energy.

❷ Use the diagram of a magnet being pushed into a coil of wire to answer the following questions. Think about the size and direction of any current produced.

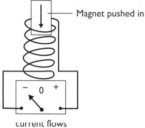

Magnet pushed in

current flows

What would happen if the magnet was
a left in the coil (not moving)
b pulled out   c pushed in faster
d pulled out of a coil with twice as many turns?

❸ The diagrams show a cross-section of a coil turning between two magnets. The magnets are standing vertically and the coil rotates about a horizontal axis. The current produced in one part of the coil is shown, as the coil turns through 360°. Copy the diagrams. Use the labels in place of A–D on your diagrams.

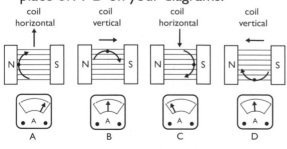

| coil horizontal | coil vertical | coil horizontal | coil vertical |

A   B   C   D

• When the wire runs parallel to the field there is no current.
• When the wire cuts down through a field a reverse current is induced.

• When the wire cuts up through a field a current is induced.
• When the wire runs parallel to the field there is no current.

❹ Copy and complete these sentences. Choose the correct word from each pair.

Electrical generators work by having a coil of wire spinning in a magnetic field. The size of the voltage induced can be increased by spinning **slower/faster**, having **more/fewer** turns in the coil and using a **stronger/weaker** magnetic field.

❺ In a simple electric motor, a coil spins in a magnetic field. What would happen to the spinning motor if the current was
a increased   b reversed?

❻ Melissa measured the voltage as a coil was spinning between two magnets. The table shows her results for one complete turn.

Degrees rotation	Voltage (V)
0	0
45	7
90	10
135	7
180	0
225	−7
270	−10

a Plot a graph of her results, drawing a smooth curve through the points.
b What type of electricity does this show?
c Annotate the graph to show a point where the coil was cutting across the magnetic field at right angles.
d Annotate the graph to show a point where the coil was running parallel to the magnetic field.
e Rotating coils like this are used to generate electricity, but if fixed wire connections were used they would twist up and break. Explain how split rings and brushes are used to take the current away from the coil.

43 Using transformers

1 Copy and complete these sentences. Use the words below to fill the gaps.

high   low   power   transformer

You can get the same .... from an electrical circuit by having a low current at a .... voltage or a high current at a .... voltage. With a.c. you can change between these difference situations by using a ....

2 Copy and complete these sentences. Use the words to fill the gaps.

alternating   down   transformer   up

The generators in a power station produce .... current. This is stepped .... to a very high voltage by a .... before it is sent through the National Grid. Other transformers then step .... the voltage to safer levels before the electricity is sent to your home.

3 Copy the diagram of a transformer. Use the labels below in place of A–C on your diagram.

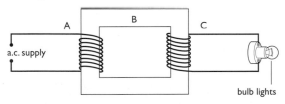

- The iron core links the field to the two coils.
- The primary coil produces a changing magnetic field.
- The secondary coil has an alternating current induced in it.

4 Look at the diagram of a 1:4 step-up transformer.

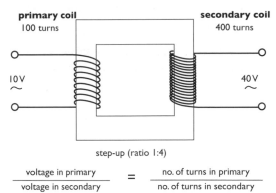

$$\frac{\text{voltage in primary}}{\text{voltage in secondary}} = \frac{\text{no. of turns in primary}}{\text{no. of turns in secondary}}$$

a What would the output (secondary) voltage be if the input voltage was changed to
   i 50 V   **ii** 25 V   **iii** 1 V?

b If the output (secondary) voltage was 160 V, what must the input (primary) voltage have been?

c Draw a scatter graph of secondary voltage plotted against primary voltage for this transformer. Draw a line of best fit through your points.

d Sketch in a second line that would show the output voltage if the secondary coil only had 200 turns instead of 400.

5 Copy and complete this table showing information about different transformers.

Primary voltage	Primary turns	Secondary turns	Secondary voltage
10	100	600	**a**
12	600	100	**b**
c	200	800	200
d	800	200	100
15	600	**e**	5
15	600	**f**	30
2	100	**g**	20
25	500	**h**	5

❶ Copy and complete these sentences. Use the words below to fill in the gaps (some words may be used more than once).

**atomic   electrons   element
neutrons   nucleus   protons**

The atom is made up of three basic particles: ...., ... and .... At the centre of the atom is the .... which contains the .... and .... The number of protons in an atom is always equal to the number of .... All atoms which have the same number of protons belong to the same .... The number of protons in an atom is called the .... number or the .... number.

❷ Copy and complete the table.

Particle in the atom	Mass	Charge
proton		
neutron		
electron		

❸ The element sodium has an atomic number of 11. Its isotopes have mass numbers of 22, 23 and 24. The diagram shows a sodium atom with mass number 23. Draw similar diagrams for the other two isotopes.

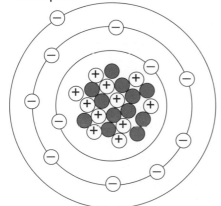

❹ Copy and complete the table showing the number of protons, neutrons and electrons in each atom. Use this information to identify the element to which each atom belongs.

	Atomic number	Mass number	Element
⚫ = neutron ⚪ = proton ● = electron	a	b	c
	d	e	boron
	f	g	h
	i	j	oxygen
k	8	18	l

5 Copy and complete the table. Then draw diagrams to describe the radioactive decays shown in the table.

Starting atom	Decay	Final atom
mass no. = 32 atomic no. = 15	beta	a
b	alpha	mass no. = 234 atomic no. = 90
mass no. = 232 atomic no. = 90	c	mass no. = 228 atomic no.= 88

45 The best radiation for the job

❶ Copy and complete these sentences. Use the words below to fill in the gaps (some words may be used more than once).
**alpha   particles   penetrating
gamma   electromagnetic   beta**

There are three main types of radiation given out by radioactive materials. These are called .... (α), ...
(β) and .... (γ) radiation. Alpha and beta radiation consist of different types of .... Gamma radiation is .... radiation. The three different types of radiation have different .... powers: ....
radiation is the most .... and .... radiation the least.

❷ Look at the diagram and use it to explain how a smoke alarm works.

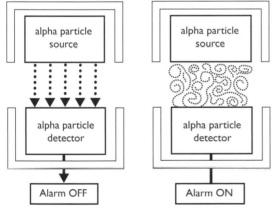

❸ Copy and complete the diagram at the top right to show the penetrating power of alpha, beta and gamma radiation.

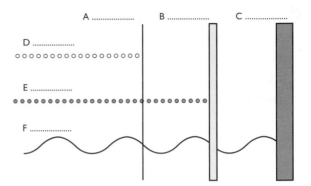

❹ The diagram shows packets of tea passing along a conveyer belt. As the belt moves along, the packets pass through the beam of beta particles.

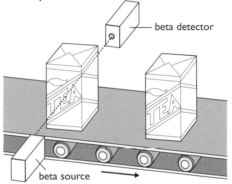

a Explain how this can be used to count the packets of tea passing along the belt.
b Explain how this also provides a way of indicating if a packet is not filled to the top.

5 Copy and complete these nuclear equations.

a $^{240}_{94}\text{Pu} \rightarrow\,^{?}_{?}\text{U} +\,^{4}_{2}\text{He}$

b $^{?}_{95}\text{Am} \rightarrow\,^{237}_{?}\text{Np} +\,^{4}_{2}\text{He}$

c $^{14}_{6}\text{C} \rightarrow\,^{?}_{?}\text{N} +\,^{0}_{-1}\text{e}$

d $^{8}_{?}\text{Li} \rightarrow\,^{?}_{4}\text{Be} +\,^{0}_{-1}\text{e}$

e The radioactive decays in parts **a** and **b** also involve the emission of gamma radiation. What effect does this have on
  i the atomic number of the nucleus
  ii the mass number of the nucleus?

1 Copy and complete each sentence using the correct ending from below.

  a Cosmic radiation …

  b Radon and thoron …

  c Coal …

  d Radioactivity …

  e Natural radioactive material …

Choose endings from

- are two radioactive gases found in the air.
- is taken up by plants and animals which may be eaten by humans.
- comes from Space.
- contains small amounts of radioactive materials such as uranium and radium.
- may be detected using a Geiger counter.

2 Explain the following.

  a Radioactivity is present inside your body as well as outside it.

  b A regular air traveller receives a higher dose of radiation than someone who does not travel by air.

  c Where you live may affect the radiation dose you receive.

3 The diagram shows the sources of the average radiation dose received in one year by someone living in the UK.

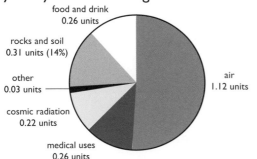

food and drink
0.26 units

rocks and soil
0.31 units (14%)

other
0.03 units

cosmic radiation
0.22 units

medical uses
0.26 units

air
1.12 units

  a Look at the pie chart, and use the figures to calculate the percentage of total radiation dose for each slice. (The percentage for the rocks and soil slice has been done for you.)

  b What is the total average dose of radiation received?

  c The 'other' figure includes radiation from nuclear weapon testing, from the Chernobyl accident, and from industrial uses of radiation. How does the dose from these sources compare with the dose from medical uses such as X-rays?

  d Someone living in an area where there is more radiation from rocks might receive a dose from this source of 0.5 units per year. Redraw the pie chart to show the dose that this person receives from all sources in one year.

4 The map shows how levels of radon gas in the air vary in different parts of the UK and Ireland.

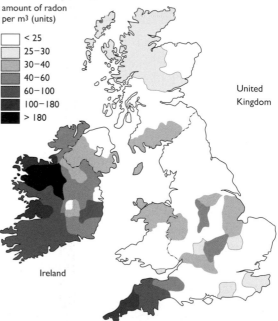

amount of radon
per m³ (units)

	< 25
	25–30
	30–40
	40–60
	60–100
	100–180
	> 180

United Kingdom

Ireland

  a Suggest why the levels are different in different parts of the country.

  b Radon is likely to be a problem in homes which are poorly ventilated in parts of the country where radon levels are naturally high. Suggest some ways in which homes could be modified to reduce radon levels inside them.

47 Radioactive decay and half-life

1 Radon-220 has a half-life of 54 s. How much of a 20 g sample of this gas would remain after
   a 54 s
   b 108 s
   c 162 s
   d 540 s?

2 Use the graph to answer the following questions.

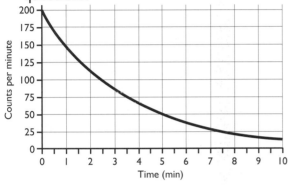

   a Calculate the half-life of the substance.
   b Calculate the count rate after
      i one half-life
      ii two half-lives
      iii five half-lives.
   c How much of a 10 g sample of this substance would be left after 10 minutes?

3 The activity of a sample of radioactive material is measured, and found to be 880 Bq. After 160 minutes the activity has fallen to 55 Bq. What is the half-life of the material?

4 The activity of a radioactive substance is shown in the table.

Time (min)	0	2	4	6	8
Activity (Bq)	240	138	80	46	26

   a Plot a graph of these results
   b From your graph, calculate the half-life of the substance
   c Predict the activity at 10 minutes.

5 A sample of rock contains fifteen times as many lead atoms as it does uranium atoms. If the half-life for uranium to decay into lead is 713 million years, estimate the age of the rock.

1 The table shows data for the decay of radioactive carbon.

a Plot a graph for this decay.

Time (years)	0	2000	4000	6000	8000	10 000	12 000	14 000
% carbon-14 remaining	100	78	61	48	38	30	23	18

Archaeologists investigating an ancient burial site find some wood. They measure the amount of radioactive carbon-14 atoms in the wood, and find that there is only 75% as much radioactive carbon in the wood as there is in a modern piece of wood.

b Use your graph from part **a** to estimate the age of the wood.

c Explain how you arrive at your answer.

2 Substances that emit gamma radiation can be used to obtain information about a patient's health. The patient is given a radioactive substance which emits gamma radiation. The substance is absorbed by the part of the body under investigation (for example, the kidneys), and a gamma camera is used to measure the radiation coming from the substance. This may produce a graph like this.

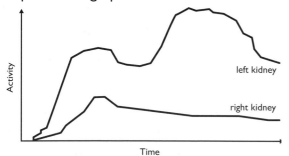

a Why are substances that emit gamma radiation used for diagnosis rather than substances which emit alpha radiation?

b What does the graph tell you about the behaviour of the patient's kidneys?

c What precautions should be taken to minimise the radiographer's exposure to radiation here?

d The radioactive substance normally used to produce gamma rays inside a patient is an isotope of technetium, with a half-life of 6 hours. Why is this isotope used in preference to one with

i a much longer half-life

ii a shorter half-life?

3 Here are two statements about the nuclear accident which took place at the Chernobyl power station in the former Soviet Union in 1986:

'It will never be possible to tell how many people have died as a result of the accident at Chernobyl.'

'The number of deaths due to the Chernobyl accident shows that the generation of electricity using nuclear power is acceptably safe.'

Take one of these statements, and use the figures in the following table to examine it critically. Do you agree or disagree with the statement? Argue your point carefully. Consider:

• Can you be sure about the data in the table?

• How sure can you be that someone has died as a direct result of the Chernobyl accident?

• How do you decide what is an acceptable risk and what is not? Who makes this decision?

	Western former Soviet Union	UK	Rest of Europe
Population at time of accident	75 000 000	56 000 000	400 000 000
Estimated total deaths 1986–2026	30 000 000	26 000 000	160 000 000
Estimated cancer deaths 1986–2026	6 000 000	6 000 000	35 000 000
Estimated cancer deaths due to background radiation 1986–2026	78 000	40 000	416 000
Deaths due to Chernobyl	8 000 to 34 000	40	2 000

1 A coal-fired power station burns coal at a rate of 30 tonnes each minute. If 1 kg of uranium when fissioned produces as much energy as 2700 tonnes of coal, how much uranium would have to be fissioned each minute to produce the same amount of electricity using uranium instead of coal?

2 Imagine that you are a newspaper reporter working in 1911. Write a report for your paper explaining Geiger and Marsden's experiment with gold foil and alpha particles and what it tells us about the structure of the atom. Remember to use language that people will be able to understand, even if they have not studied science. You may find it helpful to include diagrams.

3 The diagram shows a neutron colliding with a nucleus of U-235, splitting the nucleus and producing three more neutrons.

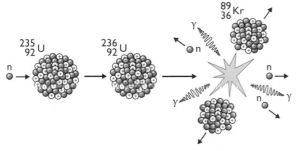

a What is the name given to this process?
b What is the form of the energy produced in this process?
c Explain how this process can lead to a chain reaction.

4 a Using the diagram in **Q3** as a guide, draw a diagram to show how the splitting of one nucleus of U-235 by a neutron can cause many other atoms of U-235 to fission.

b If each atom of U-235 that fissions produces two neutrons, one atom may cause two further atoms to be fissioned, these two may fission four more atoms and so on. How many atoms may be fissioned in total after
  i five such steps
  ii ten steps?

5 The diagram shows a nuclear reactor.

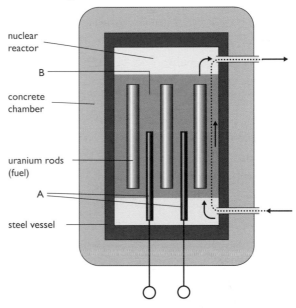

a Name the parts labelled A and B.
The part of the reactor labelled A can be moved in and out of the reactor.
b Describe the effect of moving A out of the reactor.
c Why does moving A out of the reactor have this effect?
d What role is played by the part of the reactor labelled B?

Useful equations

Forces and motion

$$\text{average speed} = \frac{\text{distance moved}}{\text{time taken}}$$

$$\text{acceleration} = \frac{\text{change in velocity}}{\text{time taken}}$$

$$a = \frac{(v - u)}{t}$$

$$\text{force} = \text{mass} \times \text{acceleration}$$
$$F = m \times a$$

$$\text{weight} = \text{mass} \times g$$
$$W = m \times g$$

$$\text{moment} = \text{force} \times \text{perpendicular distance from pivot}$$

Electricity

$$\text{power} = \text{current} \times \text{voltage}$$
$$P = I \times V$$

$$\text{voltage} = \text{current} \times \text{resistance}$$
$$V = I \times R$$

$$\text{charge} = \text{current} \times \text{time}$$
$$Q = I \times t$$

$$\text{energy transferred} = \text{current} \times \text{voltage} \times \text{time}$$

$$E = I \times V \times t$$

Waves

$$\text{frequency} = \frac{1}{\text{time period}}$$

$$f = \frac{1}{T}$$

H
$$n = \frac{\sin i}{\sin r}$$

H
$$\sin c = \frac{1}{n}$$

Energy resources and energy transfer

$$\text{efficiency} = \frac{\text{useful energy output}}{\text{total energy output}}$$

$$\text{work done} = \text{force} \times \text{distance moved}$$

$$W = F \times d$$

$$\text{power} = \frac{\text{work done}}{\text{time taken}}$$

$$P = \frac{W}{t}$$

H
$$\text{gravitational potential energy} = \text{mass} \times g \times \text{height}$$
$$\text{GPE} = m \times g \times h$$

H
$$\text{kinetic energy} = \tfrac{1}{2} \times \text{mass} \times \text{speed}^2$$
$$\text{KE} = \tfrac{1}{2} \times m \times v^2$$

Solids, liquids and gases

$$\text{density} = \frac{\text{mass}}{\text{volume}}$$

$$\rho = \frac{m}{V}$$

$$\text{pressure} = \frac{\text{force}}{\text{area}}$$

$$p = \frac{F}{a}$$

$$\text{pressure difference} = \text{height} \times \text{density} \times g$$
$$p = h \times \rho \times g$$

H
$$\frac{p_1}{T_1} = \frac{p_2}{T_2}$$

H
$$p_1 V_1 = p_2 V_2$$

Magnetism and electromagnetism

$$\frac{\text{input (primary) voltage}}{\text{output (secondary) voltage}} = \frac{\text{primary turns}}{\text{secondary turns}}$$

$$\frac{V_P}{V_S} = \frac{n_P}{n_S}$$

H
$$\text{input power} = \text{output power}$$
$$V_P I_P = V_S I_S$$

for 100% efficiency

Glossary

acceleration	The rate at which the velocity of an object changes.
alpha radiation	Weakly penetrating radiation consisting of alpha particles which are helium nuclei (two neutrons, two protons).
amplitude	The distance from the peak or a trough of a wave to the undisturbed position of a medium.
atom	The tiny particles which make up an element.
atomic number	The number of protons in the nucleus of an atom. All atoms of the same element have the same atomic number.
background radiation	Naturally occurring alpha, beta or gamma radiation from all around us.
balanced forces	When the forces acting on an object cancel each other out they are said to be balanced. Balanced forces do not affect the movement of the object they are acting on.
beta radiation	Moderately penetrating radiation consisting of beta particles (electrons).
braking distance	The distance it takes a car to stop once the brakes are applied.
cathode	Negative electrode.
centre of gravity	The point through which the whole weight of an object appears to act.
chain reaction	A runaway process in which more and more atoms fission, leading to a nuclear explosion.
circuit breaker	Electrical safety device that opens a circuit if a fault develops, preventing much current from flowing.
conduction	The transfer of heat energy through a substance by random motion of particles.
conductor	Something that will allow electricity/heat to pass easily through it.
convection	The transfer of heat energy through movement of a liquid or gas.
cosmic radiation	Radiation from space.
critical angle	The angle of the incident ray at which the refracted ray is refracted at 90° to the normal ray.
current	Flow of charge through an electrical circuit.
decay curve	A plot of the radioactivity of a substance against time.
density	The mass of substance in a given volume.
diffraction	Waves spreading out as they pass through a gap which is about the same size as their wavelength.
distance–time graph	A graph plotted to show the distance something has travelled against time.
drag force	A force which acts on an object moving through a fluid. Drag forces always act in the opposite direction to the direction in which the object is moving.
elastic limit	If an object (e.g. a spring) is stretched beyond its elastic limit, it does not return to its original length when the force stretching it is removed. It is permanently deformed.
elastic potential energy	Energy stored in an object that has been changed in shape without going beyond its elastic limit.
electromagnet	Magnet created by the flow of electric current.
electrons	Negatively charged particles found in atoms.
extension	The amount something (e.g. a spring) has stretched. It is calculated using the formula: extension = length when force applied − length when no force applied.

force	A push or a pull (see also balanced forces and unbalanced forces).
force–extension graph	Graph showing extension of spring or elastic material with force.
frequency	The number of waves passing a point in one second.
friction	Force produced when solid surfaces rub together, or when an object moves through a fluid such as air or water.
fuse	Safety device containing thin wire that melts if current is too high, breaking the circuit.
gamma radiation	Strongly penetrating radiation produced by certain radioactive substances. Part of the electromagnetic spectrum.
geothermal power	Electricity generated using heat from deep in the Earth.
gravitational potential energy (GPE)	Energy stored in an object because it has been moved to a higher position.
gravity/ gravitational force	The force which attracts two masses to each other.
half-life	The time taken for radioactivity of a substance to fall by half.
incident ray	The ray before it is reflected or refracted.
infra-red	Electromagnetic radiation given off by any warm object. It has a wavelength longer than the wavelength of visible light.
insulator	Something that does not allow electricity/heat to pass easily through it.
ionising radiation	Radiation which produces ions when it travels through matter.
isotopes	Atoms of an element with different mass numbers.
kinetic energy	The energy which a moving object has. Kinetic energy is calculated using the formula: kinetic energy (J) = $\frac{1}{2}$ × mass (kg) × (velocity (m/s)^2
longitudinal wave	A wave in which the vibrations occur in the same direction as the direction of travel of the wave. Sound waves are longitudinal waves.
magnetic field	Area around a magnet in which its magnetism can affect other objects.
mass	A measure of the amount of matter in a body. No matter where an object is, its mass is always the same.
microwaves	Electromagnetic radiation with a wavelength longer than that of infra-red radiation. They can be used for radio and telephone communication and for cooking food.
moment	The turning force which depends on the force and its perpendicular distance from a pivot.
neutrons	Uncharged particles found in the nucleus of atoms.
normal ray	In reflection, the ray which is reflected back along its own path.
nuclear fission	The splitting of a heavy nucleus to produce two lighter elements and energy.
oscilloscope	An instrument that can be used with a microphone to enable sound waves to be 'seen' on a screen.
potential energy	Energy stored because something has been moved or its shape changed (see gravitational potential energy and elastic potential energy).
power	The rate of transfer of energy with time.
pressure	The force acting over a given area. Pressure is calculated using the formula: pressure (Pa) = force (N)/area (m^2)
protons	Positively charged particles found in the nucleus of atoms.

radiation	Energy spreading out from a source.
radio waves	Electromagnetic waves with a frequency lower than the frequency of microwaves.
radioactive	Unstable atoms which emit radiation.
radioactive decay	When a radioactive substance emits radiation and changes into another substance.
reflected ray	The ray after it is reflected.
reflection	Waves which bounce off a solid surface are said to be reflected.
refracted ray	The ray after it is refracted.
refraction	The change of speed when a wave travels from one medium into another. Refraction often results in a change of direction.
resistance	The tendency of a substance to oppose the flow of electric current through it.
solar cell	Device that generates electricity from light from the Sun.
sound wave	Vibrations set up in the air by a vibrating object.
speed	The distance an object travels in a given time.
static electricity	Electrical charge that builds up on an object.
terminal velocity	The speed at which there is no unbalanced force acting on a freely falling body.
thinking distance	The distance a car travels while the driver is responding to a situation where braking is needed.
total internal reflection	This occurs when a ray strikes the boundary between two transparent materials at an angle greater than the critical angle, so that the ray is reflected back into the first material.
transformer	A device for changing the voltage of an alternating current in one circuit into a different voltage in a second circuit.
transverse wave	A wave in which the vibrations occur at right angles to the direction in which the wave travels. Waves on water are transverse waves.
ultraviolet	Electromagnetic radiation that can give you a suntan. It has a wavelength shorter than the wavelength of visible light.
unbalanced forces	When the forces acting on an object do not cancel each other out they are said to be unbalanced. Unbalanced forces change the movement of an abject, making it speed up, slow down, or change direction.
velocity	The speed of an object in a given direction.
velocity–time graph	A graph plotted to show the velocity of an object against time.
visible spectrum	White light split up into the colours of the rainbow.
wave	A disturbance which carries energy.
wavelength	The distance between two nearest identical points on a wave.
weight	The force acting on an object in a gravitational field. Weight is calculated using the formula: weight (N) = mass (kg) × gravitational field strength (N/kg)
work	A measure of energy transferred when a force moves. Work is found using the formula: work (J) = force (N) × distance moved in direction of force (m)
X-rays	Electromagnetic radiation with a wavelength shorter than that of ultraviolet radiation. They can be used to get a shadow picture of the bones in the body.